Please renew/return this item by the last date shown.

So that your telephone call is charged at local rate, please call the numbers as set out below:

	From Area codes 01923 or 0208:	From the rest of Herts:
Renewals:	01923 471373	01438 737373
Enquiries:	01923 471333	01438 737333
Minicom:	01923 471599	01438 737599

L32b

SUPERSONIC FLIGHT

SUPERSONIC FLIGHT

BASIL CLARKE

FREDERICK MULLER LIMITED
LONDON

First published in Great Britain 1965 by
Frederick Muller Limited
Printed and bound in Great Britain by
The Garden City Press Limited
Letchworth, Hertfordshire

DEDICATED
TO
111 SQUADRON, R.A.F.
WHO GAVE ME
MY FIRST RIDE AT
1,000 M.P.H.

CONTENTS

Chapter

LIST OF ILLUSTRATIONS

ACKNOWLEDGEMENTS

No book of this kind is ever completed without the help of many other people, companies and organisations. I wish to express my thanks to all those who helped in one way or another and acknowledge them by name.

As with my other books I have to thank John Taylor, editor of *Jane's All the World's Aircraft,* and John Blake, librarian of the Royal Aero Club. Without their ungrudging permission to use their records and their personal memories, whatever merit this work may have would have been non-existent.

Companies involved in supersonic flight which have given direct assistance include Hawker Siddeley; Bristol-Siddeley; the British Aircraft Corporation; Rolls-Royce; Boeing; Lockheed; Pratt and Whitney; the American General Electric; Sud Aviation; Marcel Dassault; SNECMA; Handley Page; and the Bell Aircraft company.

Other bodies which have been of great assistance have been the British Air Line Pilots Association, the United States Air Force, the Royal Navy, the Royal Air Force and the Ministry of Aviation. In particular I would like to thank C. Gregory of the Ministry of Defence (R.A.F.), late Air Ministry, for all the help he gave in obtaining facilities to visit R.A.F. Stations and fly in service aircraft.

Finally, I am most grateful to Bill Bedford for writing the foreword. That he approves this work gives it value far beyond any literary importance it may have.

B. C.

FOREWORD

SINCE man first flew, certain of his fellow creatures have been all too eager to throw a spanner in the works and say, "We must not proceed at such a pace", or even worse, "We must not proceed". Despite these set-backs aircraft speed has increased to 4,093 m.p.h., altitude to 350,000 ft. and weight to 500,000 lb., all in just over fifty years. The effective size of the globe has been compressed to bring the most distant places a matter of twenty-three hours flying time away. Man has pushed the red flag aside and taken bold strides into a future which, though knowing no bounds, has inevitably been strewn with political obstructions.

It is appropriate, therefore, that this progress should be put on record, and in this book Basil Clarke makes a valuable contribution to world aviation history by recording so effectively the background and experience leading to today's supersonic speeds. There are many lessons to remember from this past progress, the very foundation of which is military research and development. If a country finds it necessary to kill many of its major military aviation projects, this not only deals a severe blow to the civil side of aviation but strikes at the very heart of technology and the associated influence it has on other important industrial spheres within that country.

It is with sadness and concern, therefore, that one has to read the obituary of aircraft like the TSR.2 and the P.1154, which, along with their systems, were so far ahead of time. The early pioneers who provided the stepping-stone into the future had no worries of this type; in fact, initially they didn't even worry about speed. So long as the air flow over the wings was sufficient to provide lift in excess of weight they were happy.

Man was not content with this for long. Soon the quest for

speed was on, and air racing became a popular part of the aviation scene. This led to the Schneider Trophy race and despite the lack of initial Government support the famous Rolls-Royce Merlin engine began to take shape, an engine that was to play such a vital part in the survival of this country during the Battle of Britain.

From the fast, piston-engined fighters of World War II, the book traces the progress of the jet engine and its profound influences on the conquest of the air. Mention is made of the American X series rocket-powered research aircraft and their spectacular performances, leaving one in no doubt as to the immense value of such projects.

The latter portion of the book deals at some length, but very readably, with the various aspects of supersonic transport (SST), the different designs, the power plant, the pilots, problems such as the environment, air traffic control and the sonic boom, concluding with a look into the crystal ball designs of the future. One of the appendices virtually puts the reader into the pilot's seat of a hypothetical SST flight across the Atlantic and stimulates his imagination by bringing him face to face with reality.

This then is *Supersonic Flight*; a book well written and one giving a wide coverage of the subject. Basil Clarke has filled an important gap in the international aviation library and I strongly recommend his book to you.

A. W. BEDFORD, OBE, AFC, FRAeS
Chief Test Pilot (Dunsfold)
Hawker Siddeley Aviation Ltd.
DUNSFOLD AERODROME, Surrey

INTRODUCTION

LOOKING back over nearly four decades of flying I cannot help wondering if it is all worth while. Of course it is true that the existence of very fast aeroplanes enables people separated by great distances to meet each other more often and for those faced with a genuine emergency to visit sick relatives or obtain the services of the only surgeon in the world who can save their lives in time for his ministrations to be of use. But, putting these admittedly important things on one side, one is tempted to wonder if we were not just as well off when the other side of the earth was still the other side of the earth and not just an excursion of a few hours.

However, philosophising about progress is a waste of time and the only thing to do is to get what interest and enjoyment one can out of it. And certainly, if we are to fly at all, there does seem to be a case for going as fast as possible. Most experienced passengers will agree that there is nothing more boring than stooging along far too high to get any view of the scenery— unless one is crossing the Andes or the Himalayas, and that happens to few of us—so the obvious answer is to cut the journey time to the minimum, changing the old saying to, "to arrive is better than to travel hopefully."

Speed has a fascination in its own right and there has always been a queer sort of magic about travelling faster than sound. That is probably why, as soon as two-seat supersonic aircraft came into service with the Royal Air Force, I—and a number of other aviation writers—began to hammer on the doors of what was then called the Air Ministry to beg a ride. It was with some trepidation that I drove down to Duxford one day, after a medical exam that made the life insurance check-up look like a

rather amateurish piece of first aid, to report to 65 Squadron
and go supersonic in a Hawker Hunter.

The details are unimportant but we dived through Mach 1
with no bother at all, only the tiniest judder in the aircraft as
we reached the critical speed out over the North Sea where
our sonic boom would only annoy the fish. Supersonic flight was
the traditional piece of cake but, like drug-taking, it is a
compulsive affliction and it was not very long before I—and the
other writers—repeated the performance with demands for a
trip in the English Electric Lightning, capable of twice the speed
of sound. It took rather longer to achieve this goal because there
were very few two-seat Lightnings about but in the end, after
another searching medical, I got there and, this time, flew in an
aircraft of 111 Squadron, the famous Black Arrows, which had
been such a showpiece at Farnborough and many other air
displays.

We did not, in fact, reach Mach 2 but my own ride took me
to that magic Mach 1.52, exactly 1,000 m.p.h., and qualified me
for membership of that rather exclusive club—exclusive for
civilians, that is—called The 1,000 Miles Per Hour Club. Once
more there was nothing to it. Mach 1 came up on the dial with
absolutely no trace of buffeting and, with re-heat blazing, we
went on to a four-figure speed in, so far as the pilot and I were
concerned, absolute dead silence. We crossed the North Sea
and came up close to the Dutch coast in six minutes, slowing
down then to avoid breaking their greenhouse windows, and
turned for home after what, only a few years earlier, would have
been regarded as an impossible feat.

This ride in the Lightning, though accompanied by stringent
medical tests, the need to wear an oxygen mask and a long
briefing on how to use the ejection seat, was a little nearer to
what will happen when civil airliners operate at above Mach 1.
There was no question of diving to reach the speed, we could,
had we wished, have passed the transonic phase while still
climbing. The transition from subsonic to supersonic speed
would have passed unnoticed if I had not been watching the
Mach meter with rapt attention and we were sufficiently high to

have almost no sensation of movement in relation to the sea below, which, it so happened, was visible throughout the trip. The sky directly overhead was perhaps a little deeper blue than we are accustomed to seeing it and this effect will be even more pronounced when cruising at above 60,000 feet. There was, of course, no steward service as will happen in the airliners and I could not leave my seat but in every other respect this flight was a valuable foretaste of things to come. There is nothing to it except the fact that the journey is finished more quickly and the flight is much quieter than in normal airliners. And the latest jets are very quiet indeed.

Supersonic flight will soon be available to anyone who has the money and the time to buy a ticket and take the ride. But developing the aircraft and the engines, modifying the air traffic rules, solving the economic problems, devising new materials which will stand the heat stresses, improving communications so that the airliner does not arrive before the signal announcing its departure and selling the immense number of extra seats that will be available, none of these are a piece of cake. That is why it seemed a worth-while job to put this book together and cover a few of the highlights of a piece of technological progress which can have few, if any, equals in other spheres of endeavour. A great many people and organisations helped me in this work and I hope I have mentioned them all in my acknowledgements on another page. If any one has been left out will they please accept my apologies plus thanks for what they did.

Basil Clarke,
Shepperton.

A DREAM OF THE FUTURE

IT would be impossible to say when any serious thought was given to the idea of flying faster than sound waves travel, a speed of 760 miles per hour at sea level reducing to 660.3 m.p.h. at a height of 36,090 feet. The idea is certainly an old one but there was never any possibility of achieving such speeds until the jet aeroplane became well established.

Perhaps it is worth mentioning, though, that man-made objects, such as shells and bullets, were being projected through the atmosphere at supersonic speeds before man ever flew at all and there must have been some dreamers who visualised human beings travelling at immense velocities. Indeed, Jules Verne did, to mention only one. In his *First men in the Moon* he gives a graphic description of his party of explorers being fired from a cannon at Tampa, Florida, and reaching escape velocity, some 25,000 m.p.h. However, this was just fiction and it is an arresting thought that the early pioneers of heavier-than-air flight, men such as the Wrights, Blériot, de Havilland and Sopwith paid little attention to speed. All they wanted to do was to fly. So long as the air flow over the wings was sufficient to provide lift they were happy.

Looking back to those early days of powered flight I would say that speed did not really come into the picture until air racing became a week-end spectacle at Hendon and other places about 1910. I give this date because I remember as a child being taken to Hendon one Saturday and seeing a race, then a fairly commonplace thing, in which several aeroplanes were lapping at about 60 m.p.h. That was in 1912 and the sport had become well established by that time.

There were several races across Europe before the First World War and, of course, in America, but the first real speed event, the one which was to lead on to unimagined speeds, was the Schneider Trophy, first run at Monaco in 1913. No doubt it was exciting enough to the onlookers of that day but the winner, Marcel Prevost, flying a Deperdussin seaplane with a 160 h.p. Gnome engine, completed the course at a speed of 45.75 m.p.h. The following year the Trophy went to Britain, Howard Pixton winning in a Sopwith seaplane with an engine of only 100 h.p. at a speed of 86.8 m.p.h.

This was now established as the great speed event of the aeronautical world but both cars and trains had travelled far faster than the winning aircraft and even motorboats had reached comparable speeds.

The next time the race was run was in 1920 at Venice. An Italian Savoia won, but, in spite of the immense advances in aerodynamics and engines, the speed was only 107 m.p.h. and the engine power had been boosted to 550 h.p.!

The race continued to be staged at intervals of one and then two years until 1931 when Britain won the Trophy outright with three successive wins. The rise in speed was still not very spectacular in spite of the enormous improvement in aircraft and engine design. By 1931 the winner's speed had risen to something over 340 m.p.h. though Stainforth, in the same type of seaplane, a Supermarine S.6B, later took the world record to a little over 400 m.p.h.

It was during the second half of the nineteen-twenties that people began to think seriously about aircraft speeds. The Hawker Fury fighter was reaching about 250 m.p.h. in level flight with a full war load and, in terminal velocity dives, as much as 402 m.p.h. But only a superman could fly this machine and live, or so thought some of the less enlightened members of the medical profession. It was publicly stated that 250 m.p.h. was just about the maximum that the average human being could hope to survive. Very little thought was then given to the now well-known fact that sheer speed means nothing in itself, it is acceleration and deceleration that does unpleasant things to the blood stream and the not too firmly anchored internal organs of the body. As the airliners of the day were chugging along at about 100 m.p.h., and the light aeroplanes flown by sportsmen did even less, this potential human limit did not seem very important and the opinions of the doctors were of little interest to the man in the street.

A few disbelievers pointed out that, even in the latitude of London, everyone was in rotary motion as the earth turned on its axis at about 700 m.p.h., that our speed around the sun was of the order of 60,000 m.p.h., that the rotational speed of the solar system within our own galaxy might be more than half a million miles an hour and that the entire galaxy was hurtling through space even faster. The diehards rapidly disposed of that one by explaining that we had been born under these conditions and that was different. But they couldn't explain why it was different.

Probably in R.A.F. circles and in the aircraft industry there were a few far-seeing men who looked to the day when it would be possible to fly as fast, or faster than sound travelled through the air, but I cannot recollect ever hearing the suggestion that one day it would be done. And as the annual increases of speed in the air were comparatively slight it would be decades before such a thought would occur outside the realms of science fiction.

In support of this statement it is a fact that the speed record was set at 407 m.p.h. in the early 'thirties and it had risen only to about 475 m.p.h. when the war started some years later. The Hurricane and the Spitfire, the fastest aircraft of the early war period, had maximum speeds well below 400 m.p.h. and there seemed little likelihood that this would be exceeded by any large margin.

The Spitfire and the Hurricane both developed from the Schneider Trophy era. The Spitfire was designed by the same man, Leslie Mitchell, as the S.6B and used many of the design features of the racing aircraft. The Hurricane had no direct link with the race as far as the airframe went but both aircraft used the Rolls-Royce Merlin engine, which was a development of the 'R' engine that had powered the racing seaplanes in 1931.

It was due to the generosity of a woman, Lady Houston, that

these high-speed aircraft and engines ever came into existence. The Labour Government of the period was in dire financial straits with its massive unemployment at home and was unwilling to provide the £100,000 or so needed for development and participation in the race. That the nation winning the Trophy gained tremendous prestige for its aircraft industry and received useful orders from abroad weighed very lightly in the minds of men whose training had been mainly in the parochial circles of trade unionism. Lady Houston offered to provide the money and the two firms of Supermarine and Rolls-Royce were able to go ahead. No one will ever be able to calculate what Lady Houston did for her country, but it is beyond doubt that without her gift the Spitfire would not have been produced by 1940 and the Hurricane would have had no engine.

The story of the Spitfire and its evolution from the Supermarine S.6B is so well known that it would be superfluous to repeat it here. The history of the Merlin engine, however, is not such common knowledge.

This engine began life as an adaptation of the Rolls-Royce Buzzard, itself a development of the Eagle engine which had made a great name for itself during and after the First World War. The 'R' (racing) engine started life in very similar form to the Buzzard, with a capacity of 36 litres, a 12-cylinder V-configuration and supercharging. The first production racing engine gave 1,900 h.p. at 2,900 r.p.m., but Sir Henry Royce regarded that as only a beginning. Even so, it was an impressive beginning because the engine weighed only 1,530 lb. and had the astonishing power-to-weight ratio of 1.24 to 1.

Within a year or so the power had risen to 2,300 h.p. but the weight had only been increased by 100 lb. The power-to-weight ratio had improved to 1.41 to 1. Almost 1½ horse power per pound weight, an extraordinary performance. As might be expected the engine had a short life at this fantastic output, some 20 minutes only. This would just about suffice for the length of the Schneider Trophy course, but Royce would never accept such a touch-and-go state of affairs. Some idea of the brilliance and drive of this man can be gained by the fact that in just four months the engine life had been pushed up to better than one hour, an ample margin for the race.

Shortly after the 1931 race—which wasn't really a race because the other entrants dropped out one by one and left Britain without opposition and with only the need to complete the distance—the air speed record was pushed up to 383 m.p.h., almost exactly half the speed of sound.

It was to be many years before the magic Mach 1 was achieved.

2

SPEED IN THE SECOND WORLD WAR

WHEN the Second World War began on 3 September 1939 it was commonly thought that the fighter aircraft were very fast indeed but, seen in the light of history, this was not true. Britain's fastest aircraft—actually in full operational squadron service—was the Gloster Gladiator, a biplane of extraordinary manoeuvrability which could and did outfly more modern monoplane fighters, but which had a top speed little better than that of the Hawker Fury of a decade earlier. Italy, too, placed considerable reliance on its biplane fighters, the Fiat CR.42 which had a maximum speed of 267 m.p.h.

France, during her brief spell as a full-scale belligerent from 1939 to 1940, was a little more advanced in that she used monoplane fighters but even so speeds of 300 m.p.h., more or less, were about the limit. The CR.760, Caudron-Renault was capable of 534 m.p.h. but it never passed prototype stage. Germany, at the outbreak of war, was the most advanced with her Messerschmitt Bf 109 which was credited with a top speed of 428 m.p.h. though not in the early stages of its development.

The Hawker Hurricane and the Supermarine Spitfire were, of course, in production when the war started but they did not reach operational standard in the squadrons in any quantity until several months later. The Spitfire was very slightly the faster of the two in the initial form but its top speed in level flight was only slightly in excess of 360 m.p.h.

It was not, therefore, sheer speed which made these aircraft such formidable and successful antagonists for the Messerschmitts. Their manoeuvrability was certainly rather better than that of the German aircraft but the main reason for their superiority in combat lay in the skill and determination of the men who flew them.

Both these British aircraft, of which many variants were built as the war progressed, reached speeds between 450 and 500 m.p.h. in the dive but, excellent as they were in battle, the many developments did not greatly increase their speed in level flight.

In 1941 Germany introduced the Focke-Wulf Fw 190, originally with a speed of 408 m.p.h. This was later increased to better than 450 m.p.h. and it remained a formidable aircraft until Germany collapsed in 1945. Italy introduced the Macchi C.202 Folgore (Thunderbolt) in 1942 which was claimed to have a maximum speed of 369 m.p.h. in level flight. In the same year the Fiat G.55 was brought in to replace the G.50 and this aircraft could achieve 385 m.p.h.

Towards the end of the war the ultimate in piston-engined fighters began to appear on both sides. Britain produced the Hawker Typhoon and the Tempest, both with greatly increased power above that of the Hurricane and Spitfire, and also the famous de Havilland twin-engined Mosquito with almost 400 m.p.h. performance. A Westland fighter, the Whirlwind, with two Rolls-Royce Peregrine engines was produced in small quantities and this aeroplane was popularly supposed to be able to fly at 500 m.p.h. In fact its limit was 360 m.p.h. Little was seen of it, however, and the whole project was heavily shrouded in security.

Germany produced the Focke Wulf Ta 152, a single-engined fighter capable of 463 m.p.h., but this, too, barely saw the light of day in squadron service as it was too late to be of much practical use.

America and Japan, coming into the war at a much later date than the other principal belligerents, were relatively further advanced with their piston-engined aircraft but top speeds were comparable with those of the other nations.

America had a variety of fast fighter aircraft during the war years. A list of the most striking follows.

Type	Engine	Top speed	Dates
P.39, Bell *Airacobra*	1,325 h.p. Allison liquid cooled V.	376 m.p.h.	1941–44
P.63, Bell *Kingcobra*	1,325 h.p. Allison liquid cooled V.	410 m.p.h.	1941–45
P.59, Bell *Airacomet* (First U.S. jet to fly, 2.10.42).	2 × 2,000 lb. static thrust General Electric Centrifugal gas turbines.	413 m.p.h.	1942–45
XP.81, Consolidated-Vultee.	1 × 2,300 lb. static thrust G.E. turbo-prop and 1 × 3,750 lb. static thrust Allison jet.	507 m.p.h.	1945
P.38, Lockheed *Lightning,* various marks.	2 × 1,425 h.p. Allison liquid cooled V.	414 m.p.h.	1941–45
P.80A, Lockheed *Shooting Star*	3,850 lb. s.t. G.E. jet.	558 m.p.h.	1945
P.51, North American *Mustang,* various marks.	2,218 h.p. Packard *Merlin,* liquid-cooled V.	487 m.p.h.	1940–45
P.47, Republic *Thunderbolt,* various marks.	2,800 h.p. Pratt and Whitney radial.	507 m.p.h.	1941–45

Most famous of the Japanese fighters was the A6M Mitsubishi, more commonly known as the *Zero.* This aircraft, in service 1941–45, was not especially fast, its top speed being quoted as 351 m.p.h., but it was highly manoeuvrable. Other types with speeds up to nearly 400 m.p.h. in level flight were the Kawanishi NIK2.J and the Nakajima Ki.84.

Most striking of the Japanese aircraft was the MXY.8 Yokosuka rocket-driven flying bomb. These aircraft, flown by the Kamikaze Corps of suicide pilots, were driven by three 588 lb. static thrust solid fuel rockets and reached 570 m.p.h. in their final dive on the target. They were in fact manned flying bombs and it is recorded that, although the first pilots were true patriots happy to die in the service of Japan, the later crew members had to be forced into the cockpit and locked in. The MXY.8s were dropped from heavy bombers in the vicinity of the target which was usually an aircraft carrier or other naval vessel.

Russia, on the whole, was behind, technically, at that time and had to rely mainly on British and American aircraft. This is not to say that their designers were incapable of producing good aeroplanes; later they showed themselves the equals of the best, but the 1939–45 war was before the Soviet manufacturers reached their peak.

The best Russian aircraft were the MiG series 1 to 3 which reached a maximum speed of 407 m.p.h., and the Yak. 9 fighters which could attain 363 m.p.h. The latter were produced in large quantities and flew from 1942 to 1945.

In fact, the day of the piston engine for combat aircraft was ended. As early as 27 August 1939 the first-ever flight of a jet aircraft took place in Germany, very secretly. Designed by Dr. Ernst Heinkel, the aircraft was an He 178 monoplane. This machine was purely experimental but it showed the way to better things and jet flight research was a number one priority in Hitler's Reich.

It was not until nearly two years later that the first British jet, the Gloster-Whittle E.28 Pioneer, took the air with P. E. G. Sayer at the controls. There was naturally an immense programme of development ahead and it would be several years before jet fighters went into action but the doom of the piston engine for high performance aircraft had been pronounced even though there was to be considerable delay between sentence and execution.

There is a variety of reasons, probably familiar to all students of aviation, why there is a limit to the performance of propeller-driven aircraft. In brief, the blade length and rotational speed of the propeller are the principal factors. If an aircraft of given weight and aerodynamic form is to be flown at increasing speed the engine must produce more power and the propeller must dissipate that power in the form of thrust. This can be done in either of two ways, one by making the propeller rotate faster, the other by increasing its blade length. The former solution brings in the problem that the blade tips may have to run at supersonic speed and become very inefficient; the latter quickly becomes impracticable in respect of the height of the under-carriage legs if tip clearance from the ground is to be adequate.

Multiplying the engines is a partial solution but the increased drag of the engine nacelles is a serious disadvantage as is the disproportionate increase in weight of the whole aircraft. And, in the final analysis, if the airframe could be pushed through the air at supersonic speed great loss of efficiency would be ex-perienced with the propeller under compressibility conditions. So, in practice, propeller-driven aircraft are not really capable of more than about 500 miles an hour in fully controlled flight.

Even this is not quite the whole story. If the propeller problem could be overcome there is a limit to the power output that can be obtained from piston engines. Factors of cooling, weight and physical size all come into consideration and have resulted in engines of around 3,500 h.p. being the most powerful ever built and operated efficiently.

Very clearly the gas turbine had to be the next step. The difficulties of finding metals which would stand up to the enormous mechanical stresses in the heat conditions imposed were very great but once the metallurgists had overcome them the possibilities were virtually unlimited. It is true that in the early days no gas turbine could offer anything approaching the power output of a Rolls-Royce *Merlin* engine but it was not very long before it seemed that the gas turbine began where the piston-engine left off. And it offered another immense advantage to both military and civil operators. All motion in a gas turbine is rotary and in the same direction (fuel pumps excluded) whereas there are dozens or hundreds of reciprocating parts in a piston engine. Overhaul life is thus vastly increased in gas turbine engines, a point of both strategic and financial importance.

The advent of the flying bomb, the V1, which, driven by a 600 lb. static thrust pulse jet, reached a speed of about 360 m.p.h. stretched the older allied fighters to their limit. It was not until the Typhoons came into service that it became easy to deal with this particularly menacing weapon. Both the Typhoon and the Tempest could cruise at near the V1's speed and it needed only a small additional throttle opening to overtake and shoot them down.

The final phase of high speed fighters in British service came with the introduction of the de Havilland Vampire and the Gloster Meteor, both very near to the end of the war. The former, powered by a de Havilland Ghost centrifugal compressor gas turbine, had a top speed exceeding 500 m.p.h. and the latter, driven by two Rolls-Royce Derwent engines, was somewhat faster in normal operational conditions. Neither of these aeroplanes saw very much service in combat conditions but they heralded the arrival of the new generation of military aircraft.

It was at this time that the Mach meter began to be included among the instruments of an aircraft, an acknowledgment that speeds were getting within sight of that of sound.

3

NEARING—AND PASSING—MACH 1

APART from the introduction into the Royal Air Force of the Vampire and Meteor jet fighters the first indication that Britain would again have a stake in high speed flying came in an announcement from the Air Ministry on 12 July 1946. A Royal Air Force High Speed Flight had been formed in Fighter Command with the task of endeavouring to increase the performance of aircraft. Its commanding officer was Group Captain E. M. Donaldson—later to become Air Commodore and—still later—air correspondent of the *Daily Telegraph*. The Flight was established at Tangmere R.A.F. Station in Sussex.

On 18 July 1946 a Press conference was held at the Ministry of Supply in London at which Sir Ben Lockspeiser, Director General of Scientific Research (Air) said, "Flying at speeds greater than sound introduces new problems. We do not yet know how serious they are. The impression that supersonic aircraft are just round the corner is quite erroneous. But the difficulties will be tackled by the use of rocket-driven models. We have not the heart to ask pilots to fly the high speed models, so we shall make them radio-controlled."

This was the first indication of the disastrous policy which was to put Britain so far behind in the race to "break the sound barrier" and let America, still far short of British performance with jet aircraft, establish an almost unbeatable lead.

Sir Ben Lockspeiser was, of course, right in saying that new problems were being introduced. No one really knew what would happen when an aircraft flew at exactly the speed of sound. It was clear that a pressure wave would be built up on all the leading edges of the aircraft when it reached a point of speed at which the air around it could not "escape" faster than the aeroplane itself was flying. There is a limit to the speed at which sound waves—or pressure waves—can travel, a limit which varies with height and temperature.

At sea level the speed of sound is 761.6 m.p.h. This speed gradually decreases as height increases up to the top of the troposphere at 36,090 feet where the speed is 660.3 m.p.h. Above this height the temperature remains constant in what is called the tropopause and the speed of sound therefore remains constant, too. Both these speeds are taken with International Standard Atmosphere conditions but any variations from I.S.A. only produce small speed variations at the greater heights. Very close to the ground, within a few feet of sea level, temperature can affect the speed of sound and this factor proved to be of great importance when an attempt (successful) on the World's Absolute Air Speed Record was made by the late Mike Lithgow in Libya.

As the speed of sound varies with height it became necessary to use a new form of measurement of air speed when sonic speeds were being approached. Clearly, 600 m.p.h. at sea level represented totally different conditions from 600 m.p.h. at 36,000 feet, so it was decided to measure these high speeds as fractions or multiples of the speed of sound at the height of operation. The name "Mach number" was given to this form of measurement, the name being that of a German doctor of science who had done a great deal of research work on the subject. Mach 1 was accepted as the speed of sound, whatever the height, but in practice, as most supersonic flying is done at great heights, Mach 1 very often is equivalent to 660.3 m.p.h. But not always, as will appear when low flying supersonic military aircraft are discussed.

On 7 September 1946 Group Captain Donaldson set a new air speed record in a Gloster Meteor, averaging 615.81 m.p.h. during four flights over the 3 km. course laid out between Worthing and Littlehampton. The previous record, set by Group Captain H. J. Wilson, of R.A.E., on 7 November 1945, was 606.25 m.p.h., Mach 0.79. This was also achieved in a Derwent-engined Gloster Meteor. Measured against the speed of sound his flights were made at an average of almost exactly Mach 0.8.

There was still a long way to go before reaching Mach 1.0. Less than three weeks later the High Speed Flight was disbanded for the obvious reason that no aircraft existed in Britain which could improve on the performance of the Meteor.

No official aeroplane, that is. And certainly not one which could do better in level flight. But an aeroplane did exist which was to leave a trail of tragedy behind it and, at the same time, exceed the speed of sound in a dive. This was the de Havilland D.H. 108, a research aircraft which was to provide many vital data for the design of the world's first jet airliner, the de Havilland Comet.

The D.H. 108 was a remarkable aeroplane. Immediately the war in Europe came to an end all the British aircraft designers hurried over to Germany to have a close look at work which had only presented itself in the form of rumour. Among the items that aroused great interest was the swept wing research that had been going on in Germany and it very quickly became obvious that the German designers had proved in practice the theory held by most contemporary designers that high speed flight conditions could be improved by sweeping the wings back from root to tail at quite pronounced angles. R. E. Bishop, then Design Director of de Havillands and the man responsible for the Mosquito aircraft, was among those who went to Germany and he wasted no time in applying the knowledge he had acquired.

Using a Vampire fuselage, the D.H. 108 was fitted with swept-back wings and a rudder but no tail plane as it was then erroneously believed that this configuration would be a practical one. Drag would be reduced by cutting out the tail plane and a mixture of ailerons, to control roll, with elevators to control pitch could be used, the hybrid device being known as an elevon. The 108 was powered by a Goblin jet engine of 3,550 lb. static thrust, built by de Havilland Engines. It flew nine months after designing commenced.

In all, three of these research aeroplanes were built and every one of them crashed. But not before they had made a valuable contribution to knowledge about high speed flying. The first one to crash was flown by Mr. Geoffrey de Havilland, test pilot son of Sir Geoffrey de Havilland, founder of the firm. This accident happened as a direct result of lack of knowledge of what might occur at high fractional Mach numbers. The 108 had previously been dived—at a very great height—at about sonic speed, indeed, there is little doubt that it was the first British aircraft to reach the speed of sound and possibly the first in the world.

Speeds up to 600 m.p.h. + had been achieved on several occasions in level flight but always at high altitudes. Then, when flying over the Thames Estuary on 27 September 1946, Mr. de Havilland opened up to maximum speed at a lower altitude in denser air. Shock waves began to appear on the wing causing an oscillation which gradually increased in frequency. Because there was no tail unit these oscillations caused the wing to pitch in sympathy at about three cycles per second. The pitching was beyond the pilot's control and the excessive downloads proved more than the wing was stressed to tolerate. The wings broke off, downwards, and the aircraft fell into the Thames. Some of the 108 was recovered, though much was lost, and Mr. de Havilland's body was also found. From what was left of the wreck it was possible to determine with certainty the cause of the accident.

Contemporary newspaper stories suggested that the aircraft was flying at or above sonic speed at the time of the break-up but this is categorically denied by de Havillands. Nevertheless, this aircraft, flown by Geoffrey de Havilland, was the first to reach sonic speed in Europe, possibly anywhere.

A second model went to the Royal Aircraft Establishment to be test flown by R.A.F. and Ministry pilots. Before it crashed John Douglas Derry of de Havillands made a successful attempt on the 100 km. closed circuit speed record, flying the course at an average speed of 605.23 m.p.h. on 12 April 1948.

High lift devices were fitted to this aeroplane by R.A.E. and in the subsequent stalling tests it went into a spin from which no recovery could be made, probably owing to the lack of tail unit. This was on 15 February 1950 and the pilot, who was killed, was Squadron Leader J. S. R. Muller-Rowland, R.A.F.

A third aircraft was built and this, too, went to R.A.E. Its end, on 1 May 1950, is shrouded in mystery. According to the last radio signal received everything was going as planned. Then the 108 dived straight into the ground and that was all. No evidence of structural failure could be found and it was assumed that the pilot's oxygen supply had failed or run out, causing unconsciousness. The pilot was Flight Lieutenant G. E. C. Genders, R.A.F., of the Royal Aircraft Establishment.

Three first-class pilots died flying the 108 but they did establish, once and for all, that the tailless "flying-wing" type of aircraft was fundamentally unsafe unless it took the form of a long (fore and aft) delta. In that type of aeroplane the elevators or elevons were sufficiently far back to permit control which did not exist in the flying wing arrangement. So, in the final analysis, perhaps these men did not die in vain.

As early as August 1946, before Geoffrey de Havilland was killed, it was decided that the Comet airliner, also known as the D.H. 106, would be fitted with a tail unit. This fact entirely disposes of the theory, advanced by some not-very-well-informed journalists, that the subsequent Comet accidents were associated with the earlier 108 crashes. There was no connection whatsoever between the accidents.

The speed record remained in British hands for some nine months. Then, on 19 June 1947, Colonel Albert Boyd, of the U.S. Air Force, raised it by a very small margin to 623.67 m.p.h., Mach 0.82, flying a Lockheed P-80 Shooting Star powered by a single Allison J.33 jet engine. This was at Muroc, California, where conditions were ideal for the attempt. Two months later, on 20 August 1947, the record was again raised, this time a little more substantially, by Commander Turner F. Caldwell, U.S.N., flying a Douglas D-588-1 Skystreak with a General Electric T-180 engine, he achieved a speed of 640.74 m.p.h. as the average of his four runs at Edwards Base in the Mojave Desert. The Mach number was 0.84.

This record stood for just five days until Major Marion E. Carl, of the U.S. Marines, flew the same aircraft at an average speed of 650.92, also at Edwards base. The figure was now Mach 0.85.

It was stated earlier that speed records only rose relatively slowly before the war and this was equally true from 1945 onwards. More than a year went by before Carl's record was beaten and even then the increase was not spectacular. Major Richard L. Johnson, flying a North American F.86 Sabre—in full war condition—again at Edwards Base, achieved an average of 670.981 m.p.h., Mach 0.88, on 15 September 1948. The record speed was now getting within sight of Mach 1.0 and compressibility—with accompanying shock waves—was unquestionably building up on certain sections of the aircraft.

The old requirements that the speed runs should be made at a height not exceeding 100 metres still applied and there was no reason why they should not until sonic speed was reached. Then the bang would probably be powerful enough to damage or destroy the exceptionally delicate measuring equipment needed to record, to several decimal places, the speed of each run.

During 1951 the Hawker Hunter and Vickers Supermarine Swift made their first flights as did the de Havilland 110. The two former aircraft were both to break the world's speed record at near sonic speed and the Hunter and the D.H. 110 would both go supersonic in the dive at a later date. The war in Korea caused a gap in the attempts on the record but it is recorded that both American and Russian fighter aircraft dived through sonic speed in combat during that unhappy war.

For nearly five years the speed record remained at the level set in September 1948 but, on 16 July 1953, Lieutenant Colonel William F. Barnes, U.S.A.F., reached an average speed of 715.74 m.p.h., Mach 0.93. The aircraft was a North American Sabre, F-86D, flown over a course at Salton Sea, California. For the first time 700 m.p.h. had been reached.

Britain regained the record when Squadron Leader Neville Duke, chief test pilot of Hawker Aircraft, flew a Hunter, powered by a Rolls-Royce Avon engine, over a course at Littlehampton at an average speed of 727.6 m.p.h., Mach 0.95, on 7 September 1953. The same pilot took the record for the 100 km. closed circuit to more than 700 m.p.h. a few days later.

Then the record began to change hands rapidly. On 25 September 1953 Lieutenant Commander Michael J. Lithgow, later killed while test flying a jet airliner, flew the Swift at an average of 735.7 m.p.h., Mach 0.96, over the Libyan Desert at Azizia near Tripoli. This course was chosen because the intense heat near the ground raised the speed of sound quite appreciably and therefore, in fact, lowered the Mach number from the apparent figure of 0.96 and made it possible to fly faster without the complications of compressibility and shock wave conditions so very close to the ground. On this attempt the heating effects of air friction became very apparent and Lithgow, in his book, *Mach One,* said that the cockpit temperature rose to more than 180° F. during the flight.

This record lasted just over a month until Lieutenant Colonel F. K. Everest, U.S.A.F., flying a North American F.100 Super Sabre at Edwards Base, achieved 754.98 m.p.h. over a 15 km. course. (The very high speeds now being attained demanded a change of rules; and the existence of super-accurate measuring systems made it practicable to fly a great deal higher and still be correctly checked.) This attempt was the first time that Mach 1.0 —or possibly a little more—had been reached in a record attempt.

The next major advance was made on 20 August 1955 when Colonel H. A. Hanes, U.S.A.F., pushed the record up to 822.1 m.p.h. at Edwards Base. Now, irrespective of height, the absolute record stood at a speed far exceeding that of sound.

The most dramatic attempt on the record was that made successfully by Mr. Peter Twiss in the Fairey Delta 2 research aircraft on 10 March 1956. Powered by a Rolls-Royce Avon engine with a nominal thrust of about 10,000 lb. the FD. 2 made two runs at 38,000 feet and achieved an average speed of 1,132 m.p.h., Mach 1.714. This was over a nine-mile course between Chichester and Ford, in Sussex. He was thus the first pilot to take the record above 1,000 m.p.h. and he improved on that of Colonel Hanes by better than 300 m.p.h. a truly fantastic jump. Until then the biggest single increase since the war had been one of just under 70 m.p.h.

BRITAIN'S SHAME

THIS is a short chapter because what it has to say is best disposed of in the smallest possible number of words.

After the war, 1939–45, Britain had a change of government and the Labour Party came into power for the first time in many years. Although this party has always called itself progressive and, in the matter of social welfare, has perhaps justified the description, it has never been famous for scientific progress. In its wisdom—or lack of it—it decided that manned supersonic flight experiments would not proceed and opted for a programme of what could only be called missile development. This programme used the principle of dropping an unmanned "aircraft" from a converted bomber over the Atlantic and hoping that it would reach supersonic speed while sending back somewhat elementary telemetered signals recording its dynamic state.

Some tests were made and it is claimed that the vehicle did exceed the speed of sound but the information obtained was so meagre and the aircraft was not recoverable after it had dropped into the ocean that the experiments were dropped almost as quickly as the supersonic missile fell into the Atlantic. So much for a very unfortunate phase of British aviation history but it may be said that there was no lack of volunteers from both civil and military aviation to fly experimental aircraft.

Perhaps it is not fair to put too much blame on the shoulders of the government of the day because the country had only just emerged from a period of wholesale massacre and no one wanted to be responsible for unnecessary deaths. Nevertheless, Britain lost time very badly as a result of this pusillanimous behaviour. America had no such inhibitions. The X-programme was already under way and, as is described in Chapter 6, a United

States pilot reached Mach 1 just about the time Britain was thinking about its very second-rate plan.

For a country which had been the first to put jet aircraft into military service and which currently held the World's Air Speed Record this affair could only be described as ignoble and is better forgotten as soon as possible. But no story of supersonic flight would be complete without a bare mention of the work.

THE COMET LEADS THE WAY

THOUGH far from being supersonic the de Havilland Comet airliner, otherwise known as the D.H. 106, was an important step towards very high speed flight using large aircraft. Until that airliner appeared the only successful jets had been fighters, the majority of them single-engined. Now a big jump was made with the introduction of a four-engined transport plane.

That the Comet Mk. 1 story ultimately proved to be one of disaster is no discredit to the designers or to the concept as a whole. The accidents which finally caused that version of the airliner to be grounded and scrapped were due to metal failure in circumstances just not understood by metallurgists at that time. Indeed, it seems quite possible that earlier, unexplained aircraft accidents may well have been due to the same cause but several of the wrecks—The Tudor IV comes to mind—disappeared in the sea, in extremely deep water. Even if the exact position of the crash had been known—which it was not—it would have been physically impossible to have dredged up the remains and subjected them to the extraordinary examination subsequently applied to the wreckage of one of the Comet 1s.

The first Comet made its maiden flight on 27 July 1949, less than three years after the basic design had been approved. Powered by four de Havilland Ghost engines, using centrifugal-type compressors and delivering 5,000 lb. static thrust per engine, the Comet was the first airliner to incorporate the pronounced back sweep of the wings now universal in high speed aircraft. The engines were almost entirely buried within the wings, close in to the roots and the tail plane had marked dihedral to keep it clear of the jet efflux. In every other respect the Comet followed fairly conventional appearance but the absence

of engine nacelles and propellers made it an extremely individual-
istic aircraft.

The design speed was around 500 m.p.h. and this was successfully reached quite early in the trials. British Overseas Airways
ordered a number of them for their African and Eastern services
but the range of the Comet was insufficient for Atlantic operation.
At the time of the first flight it was expected that the new airliner
would go into service in 1952–53 and this hope was justified by
the introduction of Comets on the African service on 2 May 1952.

Unhappily, the series of fatal accidents began less than a year
later. A Comet 1A, en route to Canadian Pacific Airlines,
crashed at Karachi and killed all eleven occupants. This was one
of the take-off accidents which brought home forcibly the fact
that the low speed flying characteristics of swept-wing jet
aircraft were not quite the same as those of more conventional
large aircraft.

In May 1953 B.O.A.C. lost a Comet in a storm soon after
taking off from Dum Dum Airport, Calcutta. The Indian Court
of Enquiry found that "the accident was due to structural failure
of the airframe during flight through a thundersquall which was
unusually severe." All the crew and passengers, 43 of them,
were killed in this crash. Although there is no positive evidence
it is now considered possible that this was the first of the
accidents due to metal fatigue.

The real mystery of the Comets began when, on 10 January
1954, the B.O.A.C. aircraft, G-ALYP, fell into the Mediterranean near Elba while on passage from Rome to London. The
crash was not accounted for by any of the known conditions
but the fact remained that the aircraft had dropped out of the
sky without any sort of radio distress call and 35 people had died.
The world, especially the American aircraft industry, had been
watching the test flying and the route flying of the Comets with
great interest but, for the time, Britain was the only country
actually using jet airliners.

Three months later, on 8 April 1954, another Comet disappeared in the Mediterranean not long after taking off from
Rome en route to South Africa. There were no survivors among

the 21 people aboard. Clearly there was something materially wrong with this aeroplane and the British Government withdrew the Certificate of Airworthiness for all Comets, thus grounding all those that were left and putting B.O.A.C. in a very difficult position indeed. The Government also announced that an independent enquiry would be held into both accidents, apart from those run by the Italian authorities.

Then began one of the most intensive and expensive investigations ever undertaken to find the cause of an aircraft accident. No one knew where to search for the remains of the second Comet but the position of the first wreck was fairly well known. It was in very deep water and, earlier, it had not been considered practicable to try to recover any of the pieces. Now the matter was urgent and a search was made, using, among other methods, underwater television.

A number of parts of the aircraft were located and brought to the surface and, among them, was the one vital piece that provided the clue to the mystery. This section of the fuselage, near a window, showed unmistakable signs of metal fatigue so an experiment was set in motion in which a complete fuselage was immersed in a huge tank at the R.A.E. Farnborough and subjected to the pressure changes—in water—which would occur during the pressurisation phases as the aircraft climbed or descended in normal operation. In due time a similar metal fatigue failure occurred and the Comet crashes were no longer a mystery.

These accidents have been discussed at some length because, although the Comets were nowhere near to being supersonic, they did provide immensely valuable technical knowledge which was put to immediate service in the design of the next generation of subsonic airliners, British, French and American. And, of course, what was learnt then is part of the know-how going into the design of the supersonic airliners now at advanced stages of design. The whole question of metal fatigue was one about which little was known, though readers of Neville Shute's books may remember that he forecast just this kind of trouble in his thriller, No Highway, published some years earlier.

In the meantime, prototypes of the Comet 2 and Comet 3 had made their first flights and, in spite of the very adverse publicity that the type had received, it was decided to go on with these aircraft, modified suitably to prevent any future danger of the kind experienced with the Comet 1. Jumping ahead a little it may be mentioned that the Comet 4 was supplied to a number of British and foreign airlines and is still giving satisfactory service all over the world in 1965. Indeed, a military version of the Comet 4 is being supplied to the Royal Air Force to replace the Avro Shackletons of Coastal Command so the life of this aircraft will be longer than was thought.

When the British proposal to build a jet airliner had first been made public, America, normally in the forefront of aeronautical endeavour, particularly in the field of transport aircraft, decided to "wait and see." However, they were not completely idle and a design for a jet transport, which ultimately became the Boeing 707, began to take shape. The prototype did not fly, however, until three months after the last Comet accident and in the subsequent production aircraft the lessons of the Comet were incorporated. The Douglas company, too, sat on the sidelines and their DC.8, when it ultimately appeared, was a better aeroplane as a result of what had been learnt the hard way with the Comets.

Similarly, the Sud Aviation *Caravelle,* the first airliner to have tail-mounted engines, benefitted from the Comet accidents and has proved to be one of the most successful of the modern generation of jet airliners. Faster than the Comets, it is in the same speed class as the American jets reaching about 550 m.p.h. in cruise conditions.

Even more recent—and faster—are the Vickers VC.10, probably the best of the four-engined subsonic airliners that will ever be built, the B.A.C. 111, the Trident, the Boeing 727 and the DC. 9. These aircraft are all in the 600 m.p.h. + class, and, at operating height, are cruising at Mach numbers in excess of 0.9 on occasion.

Russia, too, has a fast subsonic airliner, the Tupolev Tu.104. More conventional, in that its engines are mounted in the wings, this aircraft has proved very successful on Aeroflot's medium range routes.

The era which was started by the Comets may be said to have reached its peak in 1965. The subsonic jets have naturally a very long life ahead of them but the latest of them are approaching very near to Mach 1 in their cruise state and the next advance must be to speeds well above that of sound. It has only taken 13 years from the time the first subsonic jet airliner went into service to the day when it is safe to say that the limit—in this speed range—has been reached.

6

MAINLY ABOUT X

THE United States deserved to be the first to reach sonic speed because their serious research into this form of high speed flight began as early as 1944. The U.S. Army Air Force, forerunner of the contemporary U.S. Air Force, placed a contract with the Bell Aircraft Corporation for the design of an aeroplane that could fly at or about Mach 1. The reason was that some of the very fast fighters then coming into service were flying close enough to sonic speed to experience some of the effects of compressibility and very little was known—in practical terms—about these effects.

At that time no engine or airframe existed which was capable of doing this work and it seemed unlikely that a suitable engine could be produced quickly enough. The airframe, though an admitted problem, could be produced. It was decided, therefore, to make the Bell XS.1, as it was named, a short run, rocket-driven aircraft that would be taken up to altitude and dropped into flight from a "mother" ship.

The fuselage shape has been described as bullet-like and, to a degree, it was. Wings—straight and not swept—and tail unit were completely conventional in shape. The rocket motor was mounted in the after part of the fuselage. Altogether it was a very clean design with no frills. Progress was rapid. The U.S.A.A.F. had placed an order for, initially, three XS.1s in 1945 and the first one was in the air on 19 January 1946.

The early test flights were just glides from the parent B.29 Superfortress bomber back to a landing at Pinecastle Air Force Base, Florida. Having established that the XS.1 was aerodynamically sound, it was moved to the base at Muroc, California, for powered flight trials. Muroc has been a high speed flight testing area for many years because of its natural runway of hard sand some 12 miles long.

Flight with power on began on 9 December 1946 with the XS.1 flown by a Bell Aircraft test pilot, Chalmers Goodlin. Tests continued for nearly a year and then Air Force pilot, Captain Charles "Chuck" Yeager, on 14 October 1947, became the first man ever to fly at sonic speed in level flight. By this time the "S" part of the prefix had been dropped and the aircraft was just known as X.1.

In the next three years the first two aircraft of this type were flown intensively and a speed of almost Mach 1.5 was achieved, 967 m.p.h. This did not, of course, stand as an official record but it was still an impressive performance. One of the X.1s was finally handed over to the National Air Museum in Washington in 1950.

A modified version, the X.1A, was ordered in 1948. Three of these, all slightly differing from each other, were delivered and the first one flew on 21 February 1953. Before the end of that year, on 12 December, Captain Yeager recorded a speed of Mach 2.42, or 1,612 m.p.h. and another pilot reached a height of 90,000 feet in the same aircraft. Excellent as these performances were, however, they were attended by trouble. On both occasions the aircraft went out of control and was only brought back to base after superhuman efforts by the pilots.

The tests of the X.1 series were attended by a number of accidents. Fire, due to the dangerous character of the rocket liquid fuel, was a major hazard and of the six X.1s and X.1As three were destroyed by fire or explosion, very luckily without loss of life.

The airframes were made of aluminium alloy and this sufficed for the speeds reached—but only just. Excessive surface heat was built up when Mach numbers exceeding 2.0 were achieved and the next model, the X.2, also built by Bell, was made of stainless steel. Intended for Mach 3, this aircraft had swept wings and tail plane but was otherwise more or less similar to the X.1. Although the X.2 made its first gliding flight in 1952 it was not until 18 November 1955 that Lieutenant Colonel

Frank Everest, one of America's very famous high-speed pilots, took it up on its first powered flight. He claimed to have reached Mach 0.99 on this flight and then followed it up with a number of other fast flights during 1956.

The X.2 reached a height of 126,000 feet in the hands of Captain Iven C. Kincheloe. A few weeks later Captain Milburn G. Apt flew the aircraft at 2,094 m.p.h., Mach 3.2, only to be killed when he crashed after the speed run.

The Douglas company came into the business next. That firm signed a contract with the U.S.A.F. to produce the X.3 powered by two 7,000 lb. jet engines. Three of these aircraft were to be built but in the end only one was completed. Difficulties with fitting the large engines resulted in their replacement by power units of little more than half the thrust and the specified performance of Mach 3 or better was not achieved. The X.3 was one of the ugliest aeroplanes ever built, being little more than a very long, sharply pointed fuselage with tiny wings centrally placed and a tail unit hung out on another point at the back.

The X-series of test aircraft included unmanned missiles and VTOL experimental models so there is a gap in the high speed versions until X.15. Three of these rocket-powered aircraft were built by North American as a result of a design competition initiated by the U.S.A.F. The contract was signed on 30 September 1955.

The design specification called for an aircraft of truly fantastic performance compared to anything previously required. A speed of 4,500 m.p.h., Mach 6.81, and ability to reach 250,000 feet were among the design requirements. To do these things a rocket motor of 60,000 lb. static thrust was needed and Reaction Motors—who had already been successful in earlier X aircraft—took on the task of producing it.

The motor finally produced, the XLR.99, used liquid oxygen and anhydrous ammonia as fuel and had control of thrust from half to full power, an innovation in rocketry at that time. A single-seat aircraft, the take-off weight was 31,725 lb. Take-off is perhaps a misnomer as the X.15 was designed to be launched from an airborne B.52 bomber, converted to carry the rocket aircraft beneath the starboard wing.

On 8 June 1959 the X.15 made its first glide flight. Then followed a period of rather unsuccessful launches with both of the first two aircraft but No. 2 did reach Mach 2.4 at 67,000 feet on one flight. Then there was an engine explosion which resulted in a forced landing and a lot of damage. Throughout 1959 and much of 1960 flying continued but much trouble was experienced and it was not until 1961 that the aircraft really began to show its paces. In the hands of Commander Forrest Petersen, U.S.N., and Neil A. Armstrong, The X.15 flew at just over 4,000 m.p.h. and climbed to 169,000 feet. Later the altitude was raised to better than 246,000 feet and the speed rose to almost 5,000 m.p.h.

It is almost anti-climax to go back to Britain's first flights at supersonic speed. Geoffrey de Havilland certainly passed Mach 1 in the D.H. 108 before Yeager achieved it in the Bell X.1 but this was in a steep dive and was not subject to any sort of official confirmation.

Neville Duke tells of how the Hawker Hunter first went supersonic during its test flying in 1952 in his book *Neville Duke's Book of Flight*. He describes the problem of reaching Mach 1 in an aircraft designed for a maximum of Mach 0.95 in level flight. It was necessary to dive very steeply indeed from 45,000 feet because, for a constant Mach number, the speed has to increase as altitude is lost. "Like a cat chasing its tail" is his own description and it is very apt.

He had already experienced some unpleasant effects on the controls at Mach 0.95 and the attempt to raise the speed was attended by some trepidation. From 0.95 to 0.97 buffeting and vibration were very marked and then everything became calm again. He slowed down without seeing the needle on Mach 1.0 and returned to his base at Dunsfold, only to be told that reports of a loud explosion had already come in from the area over which he had been flying. It seemed as if the Mach meter might be giving an incorrect reading and he had actually gone supersonic.

Next day he repeated the run but with the dive aimed at

Dunsfold. As soon as he reached Mach 0.97 Dunsfold radioed that a double bang had been heard. The meter was wrong and the Hunter was supersonic—in the dive.

Both the D.H. 110 and the Supermarine Swift could also pass sonic speed in the dive but these speeds were as nothing to even the Bell X.1. To be fair, it must be admitted that America did not have a production fighter which could do any better at that time but it was only very little later that the F.100 Super Sabre became supersonic in level flight.

Above, the Supersonic Swift prototype—almost supersonic in level flight; *below*, the Hawker Hunter, first British production aircraft to dive at supersonic speed

Above, Britain's latest supersonic fighter—the English Electric Lightning Mark 2—is capable of flying and fighting at speeds up to twice that of sound; *below*, the B-58 Hustler, first aircraft to make a non-stop supersonic crossing of the Atlantic

7

BRITISH SUPERSONIC MILITARY AIRCRAFT

THE British public was first introduced to supersonic flight at the Farnborough Air Display in 1952. At previous shows there had been flights which reached the threshold of sonic speed but this was the beginning of a new era.

Sonic speed was only achieved in the dive in those days and the first to startle the crowd, official visitors only on that day, was Squadron Leader Neville Duke, then chief test pilot of Hawker Aircraft Limited. He was flying an early version of the Hunter and he made his bang many thousands of feet above the field before continuing the dive to make one of the classic low runs—at near sonic speed—along the runway. The same day, Dave Morgan in the Vickers Supermarine Swift repeated the performance and, not to be outdone, John Derry went supersonic in the de Havilland 110.

So started a phase which became the most spectacular part of the Air Display for several years with ever bigger and better bangs causing alarm and dismay among the inhabitants of Farnborough and its environs but delighting the hearts of every schoolboy from six to sixty who made up much of the hundreds of thousands of people who filled Farnborough on the public days.

It will probably never be fully known what effect sonic speed with its accompanying shock waves and turbulence had on the structures of the aircraft which gave those early demonstrations but their manufacturers and pilots would readily admit now that they still had a lot to learn about design in the early 'fifties.

The climax was reached on 6 September 1952, when the de Havilland 110 broke up in the air while turning towards the enormous crowd that came to Farnborough following the press publicity about "breaking the sound barrier."

The 110 had made its bang, a really tremendous explosion, completed its fast run in front of the public and then started on a sweeping turn round the field so as to come straight over the crowd low down and at near sonic speed. In the final turn the aircraft appeared to go into a sudden vertical climb and then, as seen from the opposite side of the aerodrome, a wing came off and the entire aircraft disintegrated. Observers in the immediate area of the accident may have seen the sequence differently but that was how it looked from the press enclosure. Both engines parted company from the wreck and one fell in open ground far from any human being.

The other engine sailed—it seemed quite slowly—across the field and began to drop towards the hill between the runway and the exhibition tent, a vantage point that always attracted thousands of sightseers. Behind the press enclosure was a large marquee which cut off the view but screams told the story as eloquently as sight could have done. John Derry was flying the aircraft with Anthony Richards in the second seat and both were killed. That was bad enough for, apart from their personal charm, they were invaluable members of the experimental aviation fraternity. But it did not end there. The Rolls-Royce Avon engine struck one of the densest crowds on the hill, killing 28 people and injuring a further 63.

The cause of the accident was not disclosed at the time as the aircraft was then classified under every type of security known to authority. The facts are no longer secret, however. Contrary to the belief of many observers, some of them very highly qualified indeed, the tail did not come off first. The evidence, which included many still pictures and thousands of feet of movie film, proved that the leading edge of the wing crumpled, then the wing tips came off and finally the tail broke up.

This particular aircraft was not the one which Derry had been flying on the previous days and it seems that certain modifications made to the other aircraft had not been made to this one. How far that contributed to the break-up will probably never be known but it is an indication, perhaps, that supersonic flying at that time was still somewhat of an unknown quantity.

Regrettable as this accident was it is only mentioned here as an indication of the punishment an aeroplane had to take when so little was known about the effects of shock waves on controls and airframe structures. The "sound barrier" really was a barrier in those days. As a result of the accident no further flights at Farnborough Displays were allowed to be made over the public enclosures but, for several years following, aircraft continued to direct sonic boom towards the crowd and the creation of—usually—very loud bangs remained as one of the more popular features of the shows.

The local inhabitants around the Farnborough area did not, however, concur with this view. The public who attended on the two week-end days of each Display went there to be thrilled and, at most, they were only subjected to two or three booms. People living locally had to accept the noise for the entire week of the Display and during the rehearsal times. It was not very long before authentic complaints were made to the Royal Aircraft Establishment and the Air Ministry that actual damage, in the form of broken windows and greenhouse glass had resulted from the concussion. Ceilings, too, were brought down.

The claims were investigated and a number of them admitted to be genuine. The authorities made suitable apologies and paid for the damage whenever they were satisfied that aircraft were really responsible. At the beginning the claims were virtually all admitted but it did not take long for word to get around that there was some easy money to be made and claims began to flood in. The task of sorting them out became a full-time job for various civil servants so orders were issued that aircraft would not go supersonic over land and the day of the big bang was over, or so the authorities hoped.

During this period a controversy developed as to whether the Gloster Javelin delta all-weather fighter was or was not supersonic, in the dive. This aircraft, powered by two Armstrong-Siddeley Sapphire engines, had been the subject of a great deal of argument and it is a fact that it was never produced on the scale of the Hawker Hunters. Its protagonists swore by it while others, with or without the necessary knowledge, swore at it.

One night most of the inhabitants of south-east London were awakened in the early hours by a tremendous explosion for which there was no obvious reason. Then the facts were "leaked" and it was alleged that the pilot of a Javelin, flying on night patrol over London, decided to let the public know that his aircraft did have supersonic capability. There is no evidence that a court-martial followed but the argument about the aircraft dried up and the Javelins have continued to give good service at least until 1965. They are not, however, generally listed as being in the supersonic range.

The whole problem of sonic boom is dealt with in a later chapter. The advent of the supersonic airliner has brought the matter very much before the public of all nations and is no longer a cheap thrill for onlookers at air shows.

Very great care is taken by the Royal Air Force to avoid complaint. To such an extent, indeed, is this so, that when boom runs are made over the North Sea coastal radar is used to plan the course of the flight so as to prevent the bang from being directed at ships. Presumably a similar state of affairs exists on other coasts but inhabitants of some of the south coast towns do, from time to time, hear quite considerable bangs from aircraft flying along the English Channel.

Consideration has been given to the idea of using the sonic boom as a weapon in combat but this only applies in the case of aircraft with supersonic performance in level flight and very close to the ground. The boom from diving aeroplanes is too tightly focussed to have more than nuisance value and it is, of course, necessary to pull out of the dive at great height.

The next generation of production aircraft from the British firms which could exceed Mach 1 consisted of the de Havilland Sea Vixen, the service version of the D.H. 110. This twin-boom, twin-jet aircraft performs the dual role of defensive fighter and nuclear strike aircraft for the Royal Navy. Like all naval aircraft it has to have good low-speed handling capability as well as high top speed. A two-seat all-weather aircraft, the Sea Vixen has had long service in aircraft carriers and at naval shore bases.

Another naval strike-fighter is the Vickers Scimitar, also

with a top speed in excess of Mach 1. Although it is a vastly different aeroplane the discerning observer can see resemblances in the Scimitar to the old Supermarine Swift. Both the Sea Vixen and the Scimitar are powered by two Rolls-Royce Avon turbo-jets fitted with re-heat.

Latest of the naval strike aircraft is the Blackburn (Hawker Siddeley) Buccaneer, developed from the Blackburn N.A.39, which made many appearances at Farnborough towards the end of the nineteen-fifties. The aeroplane is powered by two Rolls-Royce Spey by-pass engines and, in addition to its excellent performance at altitude, it has been designed for very high speed attack at low enough altitude to get in underneath the enemy radar. It also has a very high rate of climb and can, of course, deliver either nuclear or conventional attacks.

All these aircraft being under a security umbrella there are no precise details of speed or range but all are supersonic.

8

ON TO MACH 2

SOMEWHERE round about 1955 the British Lion film company produced a film called *Sound Barrier* in which Ann Todd and Nigel Patrick starred. It had entertainment value without doubt but, like all products of the film world, had many technical inaccuracies. However, it did show quite effectively how the shape of the aeroplane would have to change from the straight wing configuration to the swept wing or delta arrangement and it also brought out, very dramatically indeed, that there were control problems in the speed range where shock waves began to build up that could confound even the best test pilots.

It has been explained elsewhere in this book how this swept-wing idea was followed up by de Havilland in the D.H. 108 but that company was not the only one interested. Vickers Supermarine had built the Attacker with a straight wing and, in the 100 kilometre closed circuit record attempt had reached 570 m.p.h. But this was about its limit, even if greater engine power had been made available. The next step was to produce a swept wing version which started life with a Rolls-Royce Nene engine under the title of 510.

The Nene engine was the last of the Rolls-Royce series of turbo-jets which used a centrifugal compressor and it gave a thrust of some 4,500 lb. The 510 was modified with a tricycle undercarriage and was fitted with re-heat. Incidentally this was the only Nene/re-heat installation ever made outside the Rolls-Royce organisation and it made a great impression on the public when it was flown at Farnborough in 1949 at a speed later admitted to be 670 m.p.h. (Mach 0.87) and it was, indeed, the fastest aeroplane flown at Farnborough that year. A slight dive was needed to reach this speed but once achieved it could be held for some time. By this time the 510 had become the 535.

By 1951 the type number had again been changed and the 541, or Swift as it was to be called, was powered with a new Rolls-Royce axial-flow turbo-jet engine giving 50 per cent more thrust than the Nene could do. It was this version, somewhat modified, which later took the air speed record in Libya at very near sonic speed.

The early model of the Hawker Hunter, the P.1067, was the other British swept-wing aircraft, also powered by the Avon, which was under development in the early 'fifties. Slimmer than the Swift, it was still a beautiful streamlined aeroplane in the best tradition of Hawker design with its air intakes nicely hidden on the sides of the fuselage. The day when the intake merely consisted of a gaping hole in the nose was still to come, in Britain anyway.

Various development aircraft were beginning to appear about this time which were shown off at Farnborough and most of them were very fast indeed but they were not truly supersonic. The Avro 707—not to be confused with the Boeing 707—was one of the first delta wing aircraft built in Britain and one of these put up some very high speed performances at Farnborough. They were research aircraft from which the Avro Vulcan was finally developed but very much smaller, being powered by only one engine whereas the Vulcan used four of the earlier versions of the Olympus.

Another interesting aircraft was a small delta research machine, the P.111, built by Boulton and Paul and powered by the Nene engine. Short and fat might be a fair description of the fuselage but the remarkable thing about the "Yellow Peril," as many journalists christened the machine, was its comparative silence as it made its speed runs at Farnborough, and it was moderately fast, about 600 m.p.h. Two tailless P.111s were built, followed by the P.120 with a tailplane on top of the fin. This one crashed in less than a month.

The first delta aircraft to go into R.A.F. service was the Gloster Javelin. This aircraft, whose supersonic capability is covered in another chapter, was powered by two Armstrong-Siddeley Sapphire engines, with re-heat, and it was unusual in being the first civil or military aircraft to incorporate the tail plane mounted on top of the fin, similar to the arrangement now seen in the Hawker Siddeley Trident and the H.S. 125, as well as in various American aircraft and, of course, the VC.10.

One of the most delightful-to-look-at and efficient aeroplanes produced in Britain was the Folland (later Hawker Siddeley) Gnat. Virtually a miniature swept-wing fighter, the Gnat, which is powered by a Bristol Siddeley Orpheus turbo-jet, quickly became a two-seat trainer with transonic capability in the dive. The Gnat was originally planned as a fighter aircraft which would be very much cheaper to produce than the then current transonic aircraft and it was sold, in this capacity, to certain foreign air forces. Britain preferred it as a trainer and it has proved very successful in this role. Many pilots have made their first dive through Mach 1 in the Gnat.

France took a long time to recover from the extended period of German occupation and it was not until 1950 that she began work on her first jet-propelled fighter. This was a product of that great company, Avions Marcel Dassault, and it used the code name given to Marcel Bloch when he was working in the Resistance. Older readers may recall that Bloch was one of the great names in French aviation between the wars. The fighter was developed from a private venture design started several years earlier and the M.D. 450 Ouragan (Hurricane) became standard equipment for the French Air Force, and other air forces, for several years. With a slightly swept leading edge, rather bulbous fuselage reminiscent of the Swift, and an air intake in the nose, the Ouragan was not particularly pleasant in appearance and, of course, it was far from being supersonic. Nevertheless, it was a good aeroplane for its time and it was the forerunner of a series of Marcel Dassault aircraft which have proved highly successful.

Next in the Dassault series was the Mystère. Similar in many ways to the Hunter, this fighter had swept wings, tail and fin, the tail plane was set some way up the fin, well clear of the jet pipe, but the air intake was still in the nose. In all some 600 of these aircraft—two types, Mystère II C and IV A—were supplied to the French Air Force and other countries and some of them were powered by the Rolls-Royce Avon. These aircraft had Mach 1 capability in the dive and have remained in service at least up to 1965. The Super Mystère was produced in 1955 and this was the first European aircraft to go into service as a genuinely supersonic interceptor.

Although America lagged a little behind Britain in producing jet fighters for operational use that country did not take very long to catch up. A number of aircraft were produced which followed more or less conventional lines before the F.86, the Sabre, made its first flight in 1948. This aircraft was still in use for training purposes in the United States in 1965 and, with a speed of more than 650 m.p.h. in level flight it was supersonic in the dive from the start of its long history. Swept wings, tail and fin conformed to the, by then, normal practice but the tail plane was in the conventional position on the rear of the fuselage and the air intake was mounted in the form of a scoop below the nose. It was a typical example of the old saying that, "if it looks good it is good"; a near-proverb which was soon to be confounded as the first of the Mach 2 designs began to appear on the drawing board.

The Sabre was almost certainly the first of the Western bloc military aircraft to see service against aircraft of comparable performance, the Russian-built MiG. 15 used by the Communists in the Korean War. The MiG was an excellent aeroplane but, on the whole, the Sabre proved superior, perhaps more because of the quality of the pilots when compared to the Chinese airmen who flew for North Korea rather than for actual technical advantage.

America's first truly supersonic military aircraft was the F.100, Supersabre, built by the same firm as the Sabre, North American Aviation. The Supersabre was—and is—a remarkable aeroplane. Rather similar to its smaller sister, the Supersabre has an ugly air intake in the nose but in every other respect its design is attractive. With a range of 1,600 miles without air re-fuelling, for which it is fitted, it has a top speed of 822 m.p.h. at 30,000 feet (Mach 1.18) and is powered by a Pratt and

Whitney J.57 turbo-jet which, with re-heat, gives 16,000 lb. thrust. The Supersabre was not only the first American conventional aircraft to be supersonic in level flight, it was the first in the world.

Just as Britain was producing the four-engined V-bombers, the Vickers Valiant (Rolls-Royce Avons), the Avro Vulcan (Bristol Olympus), and the Handley Page Victor (Armstrong Siddeley Sapphires), which all had speeds approaching Mach 1, so America was also active in the very fast multi-engined strategic bomber field. The Boeing B.47 Stratojet, with six G.E. J.47 turbo-jets of 6,000 lb. thrust each, had a 3,000 mile range with a top speed of better than 630 m.p.h. at up to 40,000 feet, Mach 0.95. Another aircraft from the same firm was the B.52 with eight Pratt and Whitney turbo-jets of up to 17,000 lb. thrust each. This bomber could reach 650 m.p.h. in level flight (Mach 0.98) and obviously had the potential of passing Mach 1 in a dive. Both these aircraft were of the high-wing configuration with an immense span on their markedly swept wings, the B.47 having a span of 116 feet and the B.52 no less than 185 feet! Unlike the British V-bombers which all had engines buried in the wings, both the Boeing aircraft carried their powerplants in pods beneath the wings, a practice which all the American manufacturers carried into their multi-engined jet airliner designs. They believed that this made for safety if an engine should catch fire but the evidence is not very strongly in favour of either system.

The B.47 was first flown in 1947 and was planned to remain in U.S.A.F. service until 1966, while production of the B.52— which made its first flight in 1952—continued until 1962. This aircraft may therefore be expected to have a life well into the 'seventies.

Somehow one does not regard Scandinavia as including aircraft manufacture in its variety of industries but Sweden has produced some important aeroplanes, not the least of them being very fast jet fighters. The Svenska Aeroplan Aktiebolaget, more simply known as the S.A.A.B. Aircraft Company, has been active in aircraft production since 1930 and began design work on an original jet fighter in 1946. This was the S.A.A.B. 29, a swept-wing aircraft powered by a de Havilland Ghost engine. It would hardly have been called a pretty aeroplane, with its intake in the nose and the jet pipe brought out under the after end of the fuselage but, for its time, it had a magnificent performance. Flight testing began in 1948 and it soon appeared that it had a maximum speed of 650 m.p.h., very close to Mach 1.0 at operational height. It went into service with the Swedish Air Force in 1951.

This was followed quickly by the S.A.A.B. 32, the Lansen, which was a two-seat all-weather aircraft with a top speed of 700 m.p.h. Power again came from a British engine, this time the Rolls-Royce Avon, R.A.7R, built under licence in Sweden by the Flygmotor company. An even faster version of the Lansen appeared in 1957 which used a later and more powerful mark of the Avon.

The next stage was a change to the double delta wing, rather similar in planform to that proposed for the Lockheed supersonic airliner. A research aircraft, the 210, was first built and from this was developed the Draken (S.A.A.B. 35). Still powered by the Avon, now known to have been a version with about 10,000 lb. thrust, the Draken was in the Mach 1.5 class. It first flew in 1955 and has since become a standard fighter for the Swedish Air Force.

Britain's first—and only—fully supersonic production fighter to go into service was the English Electric Lightning. Originally powered by two Armstrong Siddeley Sapphires, the P.1 as it was first called, made its initial flight at Boscombe Down on 4 August 1954. The Lightning, which has since been produced in two-seat trainer form as well as the single-seat operational version, is a swept-wing aircraft, the sweep angle being so fine that the aircraft when seen from some angles, looks like a delta with a normal tail. The production version is powered by two Avons, with an annular intake in the nose, and the fuselage, which is quite deep from top to bottom, is virtually straight-sided making the whole effect hardly an attractive one. The Lightning can reach supersonic speed in the climb with re-heat and it is capable of 1,500 m.p.h. in level flight, better than Mach 2 at 36,000 feet or above. Like all the more modern supersonic aircraft, the Lightning passes through the transonic stage with absolutely no vibration, flutter, turbulence or buffeting and pilots consider it delightfully easy to handle. Built of aluminium alloy this aircraft is suitable from a thermal point of view for its maximum speed but it has run into a little trouble over metal fatigue and some modifications and replacements have been called for as a result.

In spite of the general idea that the Russians have swept ahead of the West in technological development, created by their undoubted superiority in the early days of space exploration, this nation has not excelled in the supersonic field. Their first genuinely supersonic aircraft was the MiG 17, a swept wing single-seat fighter with a performance comparable to the Supersabre; top speed about 850 m.p.h. (Mach 1.3 at 36,000 feet).

Prior to this aircraft the designer Yakovlev produced a twin-engined, swept-wing fighter, the Yak 25, which was intended to be a counter to the American B.47 bomber. In its early stages this aircraft did not live up to expectations and it quite quickly became obsolescent. Later versions, however, did provide an improved performance and it is estimated that the last one produced could just about reach Mach 1.05 in level flight.

The first aircraft built for the Russian Air Force which could be described as competitive with the Lightning was the MiG 19. As always with Russian aircraft, there is not a lot of detail available but it is a delta-wing design and it is known to have a speed in excess of Mach 2. This product of Artem Mikoyan and Mikhail Gurevich is a very small aeroplane but it is considered to have immense possibilities of development. With its delta wing and swept tail-plane it bears a slight resemblance to the TSR.2 (referred to in Chapter 10) but it is, of course, in an entirely different class. A number of these aircraft were supplied to the Indian Air Force but their short range seems to have caused some dissatisfaction.

9

MILITARY AND RESEARCH MACH 2 PLUS AIRCRAFT

AMERICA probably has more types of military aircraft with a performance of Mach 2, or better, than any other single country. Both Russia and France certainly have Mach 2 aircraft in service but in nothing like the variety available in the U.S. Forces.

Taken in type number order the fighters are:

The F.101 Voodoo, built by the McDonnell Aircraft Corporation. This is a swept-wing aircraft in single or two-seat form for different duties, including photography at 1,000 m.p.h., at low level. Its maximum speed at 40,000 feet is Mach 1.8 and it has a good range of 2,800 miles—not at supersonic speed, of course. Power is provided by two Pratt and Whitney J57.13 turbo-jets with re-heat. Each engine develops 14,500 lb. thrust without the re-heat being switched in. The engines are slightly dropped below the fuselage with the jet pipes emerging ahead of, and well below, the tail plane.

F.104 Starfighter, built by Lockheed. Capable of achieving more than 1,400 m.p.h., this aircraft is unusual in appearance in that the wing is set well aft and has something akin to delta shape, the tips of the triangles being cut off parallel with the fore and aft centre line. A swept fin is included but no tailplane. The intakes for the single General Electric J.79 turbo-jet, which produces 15,800 lb. thrust, are on the sides of the fuselage slightly ahead of the wing roots. The jet pipe comes straight out of the tail.

Originally built for the U.S.A.F. this aircraft has also been built under licence in Canada, Germany, the Netherlands, Italy and Japan and the air forces of these countries are equipped with the 104 in some quantity. One version of this aircraft at one time held both the speed and altitude records, at 1,404 m.p.h. and 103,389 feet respectively.

F.105, Thunderchief, built by the Republic Aviation Corporation. An all-weather tactical fighter, it can also carry up to 6 tons of weapons and has a bomb bay longer than that of the original Flying Fortress. The 105 is a conventional-looking swept wing aircraft with a single Pratt and Whitney J.75 giving 26,500 lb. thrust with re-heat and it has a speed of Mach 2.25 at 38,000 feet with Mach 1.25 at sea level.

F.106, Delta Dart, built by General Dynamics/Convair. This aircraft is a development from the F.102 Delta Dagger which was the world's first supersonic all-weather interceptor and first to use the "Area Rule" the design system which includes a waist along the fuselage to improve the airflow along the aircraft at supersonic speeds. In the United States this is, quite understandably, likened to the container for a world-famous soft drink and area rule aircraft are usually referred to as "Coke bottles." The F.106A at one time held the air speed record at 1,525.9 m.p.h.

F.4, Phantom, built by McDonnell Aircraft Corporation, is the fastest tactical fighter currently in production in 1965. It set a new air speed record in November 1961, of 1,606.48 m.p.h. (Mach 2.23) and incorporates blown flaps on both leading and trailing edges, thus giving a lower stalling speed than its delta-wing would otherwise have. Powered by two General Electric J79 turbo-jets, the Phantom is claimed to have a top speed in excess of Mach 2.5 and a ceiling of 66,000 feet. It has a tail plane with slight anhedral angle (the tips are lower than the roots), the intakes are on the side of the fuselage and the jet pipes emerge forward of, and below, the tail unit. The fin is steeply swept.

The Phantom has been ordered for the Royal Navy and the Royal Air Force in quantity and it is likely it will be powered by Rolls-Royce Spey engines for British use. Some fears have been aroused at the possible cost of £100,000,000 for the modifications needed for the Spey engines and the matter is under consideration at the time of writing. Like all the modern strike aircraft it carries an enormous load of electronics for navigation and weapon control.

In the early stages of flight testing is the variable geometry F.111A, originally known as the TFX. This aircraft, a product of General Dynamics/Fort Worth, is generally supposed to have some of the qualities of the TSR.2 and it is now expected to replace the TSR.2 in the Royal Air Force. The wing roots are typical of a slender delta but the outer section of the wings can stand more or less straight out for take-off and low-speed operation, folding back to make a small angle with the fore and aft centre line at high speed. The F.111A is claimed to have a top speed of 1,850 m.p.h. (Mach 2.8) and an operational ceiling of 60,000 feet with a range described as transoceanic. It is also intended to have supersonic dash performance at ground level and to be equipped with contour following radar/autopilot comparable with that in the TSR.2. In the prototype, power is derived from two Pratt and Whitney TF30 turbo-fans (by-pass) giving, with re-heat, 30,000 lb. thrust each. This is the first American military aircraft of high Mach number performance to be fitted with turbo-fans.

Like the TSR.2 the F.111A has a tail unit and the intakes are in the side of the fuselage. The main wings are in the high-wing formation and this results in an unusual but pleasing appearance.

Among the American bombers in the Mach 2 class are the B.58 Hustler type built by General Dynamics/Fort Worth. The fastest nuclear bomber in the world, this aircraft is powered by four General Electric J.79.5 turbo-jets in separate pods beneath the delta wings. The total thrust available is 62,400 lb. and re-heat is also fitted. The maximum speed claimed is 1,380 m.p.h. at 35,000 feet, fractionally above Mach 2.

This aircraft achieved two striking records. The first was when it was flown across the Atlantic from the U.S.A. to Paris for the 1963 Air Show and, with several flight re-fuellings, made the trip non-stop in just over three hours, flying at an average speed of more than 1,100 m.p.h. Unfortunately, this aeroplane crashed at the Paris Show for reasons which have not been disclosed. Another B.58 did the same thing at the 1965 Paris Show. The second flight which obtained well-deserved publicity was a non-stop trip from Tokyo to the American air base at Greenham

Common in Berkshire on 16 October 1963. Again flight re-
fuelling was employed; in all, five contacts were made with
KC.135 Stratotankers. It was intended that the 8,028 mile trip
should be done at exactly 1,000 m.p.h. but minor engine trouble
slowed the Hustler down on the last leg of the flight and the
average speed came out at 936 m.p.h.

Major S. J. Kubesch, U.S.A.F., was in command of this flight
which cut in half the previous record for the journey set by an
English Electric Canberra in 1955. The total time for the flight
was 8 hours 35 minutes and it really demonstrated that sustained
supersonic flight was no longer a dream. The Hustler is the
third of the long range nuclear bombers in the United States
Strategic Air Command.

Britain has only one native product in the Mach 2 group, the
Lightning already covered in a previous chapter. France is almost
better equipped. The Marcel Dassault firm produced another of
the Mirage series, the IV A, which was designed to carry the
nuclear weapon independently developed by France. This delta
bomber, which is powered by two Atar 9D turbo-jets of 14,900
lb. thrust each, is capable of speeds in excess of Mach 2. The
Mirage IV A is a scaled up version of the Mirage III fighter and
almost exactly resembles it.

Russia never gives anything away about its military aircraft but
facts do leak out and some details are available of a Mach 2 interceptor, the MiG. 23, code name Flipper. This is a delta with the
wings set well back along the 65 feet fuselage. The span appears
to be about 30 feet. A swept tail plane is used, secured to the outer
sides of the twin jet pipes. The fin is steeply swept and the air
intake for the two engines is an annular opening in the nose.

The MiG. 23 is believed to be powered by two turbo-jets of
12,500 lb. thrust each, it has a service ceiling of 60,000 feet
and is claimed to be capable of reaching Mach 2 with two, quite
large, air-to-air missiles carried beneath the wings. The range
of the aircraft is believed to be small as it is intended for point
defence and it was considered ideal to intercept—and shoot
down if necessary—the unarmed, slow, U.2 spy-planes the
Americans used to send over Russia.

Above, Buccaneer S 2 and S 1, low-level strike reconnaissance aircraft; *below*, the Hawker Siddeley V/Stol tactical strike aircraft can reach supersonic speed in the dive. The wing markings are those of the Tripartite Squadron

Above, the de Havilland 108 research aircraft, the first machine to reach Mach 1 in a dive; *below*, the Avro 707A, built for high-speed research in delta wing design

There is also a Russian supersonic bomber, code-named the Bounder. With four turbo-jets, two in pods beneath the delta-wings and two mounted on the wing tips, this aircraft, which has a conventional swept-tail unit, is reputed to fly at between Mach 1.5 and Mach 2 but details are scarce.

It would seem that at least three of the great military powers, U.S.A., France and Russia, do not agree with certain elements in Britain that the day of the manned, high speed bomber is past.

Mach 2 is more or less of a milestone in the development of supersonic aircraft for it is there or thereabouts that aluminium alloys cease to be satisfactory materials for airframes owing to the "thermal barrier", the point at which air friction makes airframes exceptionally hot and affects the characteristics of the metal. In this respect there is little difference between the conditions affecting a fighter or an airliner, assuming, as it is reasonable to do, that the most efficient aerodynamic shapes will be used in every type of aircraft.

The accompanying illustration shows how the strength-to-weight ratio changes with rising temperature in a number of

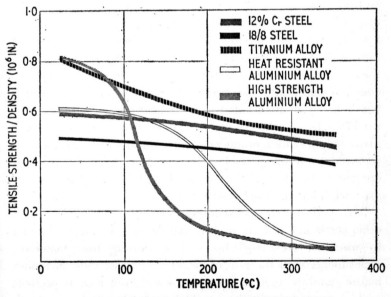

STRENGTH/WEIGHT RATIO AT ELEVATED TEMPERATURES

materials and it is clear from this that heat-resistant aluminium alloys provide quite satisfactory results up to the maximum temperature (about 120° C.) to which most of the airframe of a Mach 2.2 aircraft will be subjected. Certain leading edges rise to 155° C. and the curve suggests that steel or titanium offer more satisfactory results in these positions. But when a Mach 3 aircraft is being considered, with its skin temperature at the 300° C. mark it is obvious that only steel or titanium will retain their strength characteristics at these temperatures. Inconel alloys have even greater creep resistance at high temperatures but the density of these materials makes them unpractical for use in large quantities in an aircraft where weight is a primary factor. It is indeed claimed that titanium is superior at Mach 3 to aluminium at very much lower Mach numbers and the set of curves does support this claim.

So aeroplanes which would fly appreciably faster than Mach 2.2 presented many new problems to the designer. Not only did he have to make exhaustive wind tunnel tests of models to determine the best aerodynamic shape for his aircraft but also he had to subject a variety of materials—including non-metallic materials—to meticulous tests of strength under conditions of heat. Having found suitable materials he then had to pass them over to research engineers who had to evolve means of machining them and that was not always easy. It is true that beryllium does not come into the supersonic range of aircraft materials but it has been used extensively in aviation and that gave the machine shop engineers more than enough headaches. When machined, beryllium produced toxic by-products which had to be removed from any possible risk of contact with the machine operators. This is a good example of the sort of difficulties new materials sometimes bring with them.

It is well known that stainless steel is, by comparison with other steels and, indeed, most of the "standard" metals difficult to machine. New techniques, new cutting tool materials, experiments with the rate of cutting, cost vast sums of money before stainless steel was conquered and even now it presents problems—as does titanium—which make the works manager's job harder. These metals are costly, sometimes very costly, so machining processes had to be devised which would cut waste to a minimum.

The Boeing company has expended a great deal of money on experiments with titanium, a metal which has gradually taken a more important place in subsonic aircraft. About 1½ million pounds of this metal was used in the B.52 bombers alone and all that experience has resulted in knowledge of how to mill, spin, drill, ream, grind and shear titanium in the most efficient way possible. Boeing is, of course, not the only company to work on this kind of problem; all the American firms interested in Mach 3 aircraft have done the same. Not so much has been done in Britain on titanium but this country could reasonably claim to lead the world in stainless steel developments.

Firth-Vickers Stainless Steels Ltd. is a company which has been in the forefront of development of stainless steel for aircraft use and their latest product, F.V. 520(B) has been accepted by the aeronautical industry as being the most advanced alloy in this range. This metal, which can be machined as other stainless steels can, may also be produced in the form of forgings, rolled bar or plates and this facility helps to reduce waste in processing the metal for specific parts of an aircraft. This steel will find a place in the Concord structure and, had it been produced sooner, it is virtually certain that the Bristol T.188 would have been made of it.

The 188 must have mention here in spite of the fact that it apparently did not quite measure up to the demanding standards of the thermal research for which it was designed. Intended to be a flying test bed for Mach 3 aircraft, it was built of Firth-Vickers 448 stainless steel which the company admits was not so suitable for manipulating and forming as the later product. Coupled with the fact that the Gyron engines did not develop sufficient thrust for the planned programme the T.188 was not too successful and its test life was somewhat curtailed. It may be recalled that an early American jet fighter was known as the Thunderjet. The T.188 was christened the "Blunder Jet" by certain unkind critics but it did provide much useful information and from its flying emerged—according to Firth-Vickers—the fact that it would have been a much better aeroplane if F.V. 520(B) had been its structural material. So, in a negative sort of way, valuable guidance to the suitability of materials was obtained from this rather expensive experiment.

Britain was not alone in suffering failure in the design of Mach 3 aircraft. Right back in 1954 the Americans decided that the successor to the B.52 would have to be a very advanced aeroplane capable of flying great distances and reaching then unheard-of speeds. Numerous designs were considered and the XB.70 Valkyrie was chosen. This futuristic aeroplane was to be designed and built by North American Aviation and even when it was little more than the traditional sketch on the back of an envelope there was an idea that it would provide the basis of the future supersonic airliner.

The Valkyrie, a delta with the wings right aft and the pitch controls mounted on tiny wings right forward, was the realisation of a design aeronautical engineers had been playing with—but never very successfully—since the earliest days of powered flight. It will be remembered that several of the very early biplanes had the elevator on a structure well ahead of the wings with the rudders on a similar structure aft. There is no logical reason why the arrangement should not work but it has never been popular and the XB.70 is no exception to that general rule.

The length of the aircraft is given as 185 feet, the wing span is 120 feet and power is provided by six General Electric YJ.93.3 turbo-jets, each of 33,000 lb. thrust and each with re-heat to provide additional thrust. The planned speed was to be greater than 2,000 m.p.h. and the ceiling 70,000 feet. The maximum take-off weight is given as 550,000 lb., or about 250 tons.

Time went on and the XB.70 ran into trouble. The fuel tanks leaked, and went on leaking. The new materials were giving teething troubles on an unprecedented scale. Gradually hopes dwindled and, finally, before even the first prototype had ever left the ground, the XB.70 was dropped as a military aircraft and the order was reduced to two prototypes for research purposes.

But it should not be thought that all the effort that went into this design was wasted. It is true that the North American Aviation design for a supersonic transport, based very largely on the XB.70, was completely dropped out of the race, but some of the work has borne fruit in the very latest Mach 3 aircraft now finding their way into the U.S. Air Force.

One of these is the SR.71, a Mach 3 long-range strategic reconnaissance aircraft. Still very much on the secret list, there is little information available about it except that it is being built by Lockheed and will be powered by two or more Pratt and Whitney J.58 engines of 30,000 lb. thrust each. It is suggested in certain American quarters that it may have a role as a bomber as well but there is nothing positive on this idea. There is, however, one remarkable factor about it which is most unusual. It has been officially stated that the design was initiated in February 1963, and flight testing of operational aircraft was due to begin in "early" 1965. As this statement came from the lips of no less a person than President Lyndon B. Johnson himself it must be assumed to be substantially correct and it raises the point that the speed with which the design and construction work was being done was comparable with the speed of the aircraft itself. Two years from initial design to the start of flight testing is something not associated with the development of modern aircraft with all their costly complexities.

It is therefore being guessed that the SR.71 is a close relation of the YF.12A the existence of which was disclosed, also by President Johnson, at a news conference in Washington on 29 February 1964. Then known as A.11, this aircraft was also a Lockheed product and some facts have been published. The length is about 90 feet, the span of the rear-positioned delta wing is about 55 feet and power is provided by two Pratt and Whitney J.58 engines giving a total of 60,000 lb. thrust without re-heat being switched on. Unlike normal American practice the engine nacelles are fitted into the wings and each one carries a fin and rudder over the jet pipe. Ceiling is quoted as 80,000 feet and the range, rather vaguely, as several thousand miles. The YF.12A carries a crew of two and is believed to have a very sophisticated weapon system, and now holds the world's speed record.

In the experimental field there are several aircraft, British and French, in the vertical take-off group, which have supersonic performance. First, and clearly foremost, is the Hawker P.1127, recently given the name Kestrel. It is difficult to say that the Kestrel is purely experimental because it has facilities for a weapon system and has recently been stated to be on order for the Royal Air Force. A squadron of these aircraft is being tried out for evaluation purposes by a mixed group of British, American and German Air Force personnel, based at the private airfield of Hawker Siddeley at Dunsfold in Surrey.

The P.1127, which looks very similar to other swept-wing fighters, is powered by a Bristol-Siddeley Pegasus turbo-jet engine with vectored thrust. This means that air from the compressor is fed into nozzles on each side of the fuselage after being burnt with fuel in a burner system similar to that employed for re-heat. The turbine exhaust is fed into split jet pipes which also emerge through nozzles further aft in the sides of the fuselage. These nozzles can be rotated so as to direct the thrust from very slightly ahead, through the vertically downward position to the more normal flow, horizontally aft.

By directing the flow downwards the aircraft can be lifted vertically into the air with no forward speed whatsoever. Then the nozzles are moved slowly until they are pointing backwards and the aircraft moves forward with the wings providing lift in a conventional manner. When the aircraft is in the vertical take-off condition the control surfaces have no effect so a jet reaction control system is introduced by which jets of gas, in variable quantity, are expelled from the nose and tail, and from the wing tips. These jets are controlled by the normal correcting movements of the stick, just as would occur in forward flight in the conventional mode. It may be said that the development of this control system was beset with problems but they were overcome and the P.1127 is now as easy to fly as a normal aeroplane.

Its speed range is remarkable. From 25 m.p.h. BACKWARDS

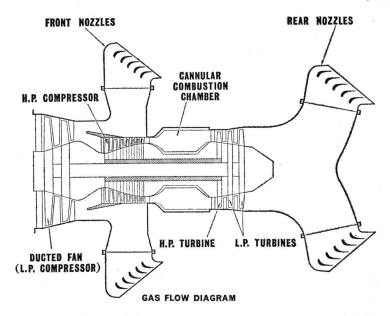

GAS FLOW DIAGRAM

to a little more than Mach 1 in a gentle dive is something no other aeroplane has been able to do.

Apart from control by jets there was another difficulty not met with in conventional aircraft. The gyroscopic effect of a turbine engine is quite considerable and would have an adverse effect on the handling of the P.1127 under hovering conditions. Bristol-Siddeley therefore modified the turbo-fan engine so that the high and low pressure compressor/turbine spools rotated in opposite directions and completely eliminated this trouble.

The government of the day—and Hawker Siddeley—wanted to use a development of the P.1127 as a replacement for the then ageing Hunters but it was considered that the defence needs would not be met by yet another aircraft which was only supersonic in the dive. So a contract was awarded to the Hawker firm to design and produce a number of prototypes of the P.1154, a similar but larger aeroplane which would have Mach 2 capability at least and could carry a weapons system that would meet modern needs. Hawker Siddeley carried out their part of the bargain but a change of government took place before any firm order for production aircraft was placed and, early in 1965, the Labour Party then in office announced that no further work would be done on the P.1154 but that Kestrels would be ordered. This was an extraordinarily backward step for, good as the Kestrel is, its suitability for anything other than what has come to be known as a bush-fire war seems to be highly questionable.

The other project is an Anglo-French one, also in the vertical take-off and landing group. Rolls-Royce had pinned its faith in the direct lift engine as distinct from the vectored thrust system and, for many years, great effort had been devoted to producing an ultra-lightweight engine with quite fantastic power-to-weight ratios. This resulted in the production of the RB.162 engine which delivers a thrust sixteen times its own weight!

Marcel Dassault have adapted a Mirage III to be fitted with eight of these engines for use only during take-off and landing at fields where normal conditions do not apply. Power for forward flight is obtained in the usual way; the lift engines are shut down and the intake and exhaust ports closed to present a smooth surface to the air stream over the fuselage.

There is much to be said for this method of vertical take-off because the transition stage can be done with full vertical lift and the lift engines need not be closed down until the aircraft has developed full control in conventional flight conditions. On the other hand, eight of even these lightweight engines must use up a valuable proportion of the available "payload", reducing fuel or weapon carrying capacity, a situation which arises to a less degree in the P.1127 and P.1154 concepts. The Mirage III converted for VTOL will still be supersonic but no plans have been announced for the use of this system in larger, faster aircraft—yet.

No account of the growth of supersonic flying would be complete without some reference to the facilities needed on the ground to aid research and development. As the scope of flying has widened so the cost, variety and size of the testing establishments has increased. Wind tunnels used to be small, gentlemanly affairs in which air speeds of a few hundred miles an hour were produced and comparatively simple models examined in them.

Now a wind tunnel is a gigantic place which may have to house a complete engine nacelle such as the vast piece of hardware seen on the YF.12A. Wind speeds of up to 3,000 m.p.h. have to be produced, fuel supplies have to be available and a multiplicity of control systems must be accommodated, all without upsetting the smooth flow round the object under test. Computers are needed to analyse the variety of signals produced simultaneously by the test item and it may be necessary to install closed circuit television cameras in the tunnel to get visual checks of some experiment.

A complex of such tunnels is installed at the Air Research Association near Bedford and the facilities include a tunnel with an airspeed range from 200 to 1,000 m.p.h. and a working section 9 feet by 8 feet. The next tunnel has a section of $2\frac{1}{2}$ by $2\frac{1}{4}$ feet and in this one wind speeds from 1,000 to 2,500 m.p.h. are obtainable. The last one is somewhat smaller but its wind speed is 3,000 m.p.h. and plans exist to step this up still higher.

The power required to drive air through these tunnels is very great indeed and, although there are many other ways of consuming electricity at Bedford, the wind tunnels are responsible for a large proportion of the £100,000 electricity bill which the Association pays every year. The capital investment for this equipment was £1,250,000. Figures of this sort go some way to explaining why modern aircraft are so extremely expensive.

In addition to these installations, all the aircraft companies have their own huge testing outfits and Farnborough probably exceeds them all in its complexity of equipment. Recently opened there is the hall in which a complete Concord will undergo its tests to destruction and a variety of other tests which will include its subjection to the heat cycles that will occur from before take-off, through the climb, transition to supersonic speed, cruise, descent and return to subsonic flight and finally to landing. And in operational conditions the ground temperature can vary from about —40° C. in Canada to +50° C. at, say, Abadan. The cost of this installation has run into millions of pounds and its running costs will also be staggering. The amount of power needed to heat up the entire Concord airframe to

120° C.—as will happen in supersonic cruise—will tax the National Grid more than a little.

In America the National Aeronautics and Space Administration has even bigger installations and much of the plant in them is tied to supersonic flying in one form or another. The investment in equipment, quite apart from the colossal payroll for those employed, must be one of the biggest capital tie-ups in the world, certainly greater than that of any other single industry. And the costs have rocketed since supersonic flying arrived because of all the new and complex problems that had to be solved—and still have to be solved.

10

THE TSR.2

THE never-ending battle between offence and defence becomes
very apparent in air attack. The ability of fighter aircraft to fly
at immense heights and at high Mach numbers makes attack
by manned bombers a hazardous proposition and this stalemate
resulted in an increasing faith in missile delivery of warheads.
Long-range radar and anti-missile missiles have made that form
of attack less attractive and there is positive evidence that at
least some of the warheads delivered by rockets soaring into
space will not reach their destinations.

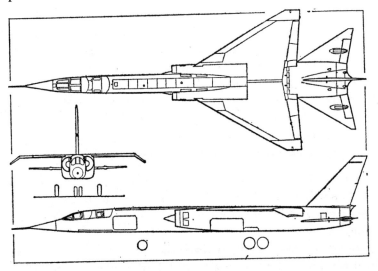

Last published general arrangement of the TSR.2

Consequently it began to appear that low-level attack, at
very high speed, would have the best chance of evading the radar
defences. Ground defence capable of coping with this type of

attack—if any kind of advance warning could be achieved—
would be remarkably expensive and, often, ineffective. Insofar
as any form of defence can ever be discounted it did seem that
protection against really low, high-speed penetration would be
almost negligible so, in 1959, the British Government awarded
a design contract to the Vickers-Armstrong and English Electric
groups. (This was before the merger which brought the firms
together as the British Aircraft Corporation.)

The role of the Tactical-Strike-Reconnaissance aircraft,
designated as TSR.2, was an all-embracing one as appears below.
The TSR.2 was required to undertake:

1.   All-weather day and night reconnaissance.
2.   Conventional strike against point targets with rockets,
      free-fall bombs or guided weapons.
3.   Nuclear strike.

It was required to have:

(a) Short take-off and landing capability from airstrip[s]
    suitable for Dakotas (over 1,000 of these exist within
    the N.A.T.O. area alone).
(b) Long ferry range.
(c) Supersonic flight ability of Mach 2+ at altitude and
    supersonic dash at low level.
(d) Deep penetration at ultra low level.
(e) A high degree of self-containment at dispersal.

Given the abilities listed the TSR.2 would be both a tactical-
nuclear-strike-aircraft and also a carrier of high-yield nuclear
weapons, thus bringing it into the strategical bomber class as
well.

Another requirement, perhaps the most difficult of all, was
that the TSR.2 must be capable of following the contours of the
terrain when flying "on the deck". Without this capability
there would be points along a flight when it would be picked up
by the defence radar but the attainment of this ideal called for the
inclusion of some of the most sophisticated radar ever devised to
control the autopilot. Flight would have to be completely

automatic during any phase of "contour chasing" at low altitude as no human pilot could possibly retain manual control for very long under these exacting conditions. Even as passengers the crew would undergo excessive "G" stresses when making a supersonic dash near the ground.

Bristol Siddeley received a contract to provide the engines for the TSR.2 and the Olympus, or a developed version of it, which was already in service in the Avro Vulcan V-bombers, was chosen.

It was realised from the beginning that the cost of designing an aircraft of such versatility would be very great indeed but the philosophy was that it was better to pay a high price for one machine that could complete its mission than a lower price for a number of, probably subsonic, cheaper aircraft which would all be shot down before finishing the job. That the TSR.2 price has rocketed to an all-time record of perhaps £5,000,000 per aircraft has caused tremendous government unhappiness but the argument is probably still sound.

Even as early as 1959 it was a fairly straightforward task to design and produce an aircraft with some, if not all, of the virtues demanded. Given an airframe of the right shape and engines of sufficient power the high-speed performance could be offered at high altitude and low-level supersonic dash could follow more or less easily. STOL capability, coupled with supersonic performance, was quite another matter but it was obviously necessary if the TSR.2 was to be used as an army tactical support aircraft.

Long range was another factor which had not in any previous concept of tactical strike aircraft been associated with very high-speed performance but the immense cost of the TSR.2 made it essential that it should be capable of rapid movement from one theatre of combat to another if the size of the force was to be kept within economic bounds.

The ability to follow the contours of the terrain—at high speed—was possibly the most difficult requirement as this demanded the ultimate in electronic devices, radar to spy out the ground ahead, a computer system to translate the radar data into signals to control the autopilot, and an autopilot installation giving instant response so that the control surfaces would do their job in time. At sonic speed at sea level the aircraft would be travelling at 1,114 feet per second with ground clearance of, at best, a few hundred feet. The need for instant response of the entire airframe to signals derived from the radar is more than clear. The attaining of standards of electronic control far transcending anything achieved previously set a task for the engineers that was without parallel.

The magnitude of the task is exemplified by the fact that more than 1,000 different manufacturing companies finally became involved in the project and, according to the Minister of Aviation in 1964, 15,000 people were employed in one way or another.

Primary work was concentrated at the English Electric plant at Preston and the Vickers factory at Weybridge but the sub-contractors were spread over the length and breadth of the British Isles.

The entire project is naturally shrouded in secrecy and likely to remain so long after this book appears but general facts have been published. They are especially interesting because much of the data applies equally to most—if not all—other aircraft with Mach 2+ performance, military aircraft, that is.

Dimensions have not been released but it is estimated that the wing span is about 35 feet and the overall length about 90 feet. The leading edges of the delta wing are swept back at an angle of somewhere near 60°, the wing is of thin section, with its tips deflected downwards to offset the dihedral effect of the delta planform.

It used to be said that if an aircraft looked right it was right and that was often true. Modern developments have tended to question this proverbial statement and if the TSR.2 relied on its looks for efficiency its political critics would be fully justified in wanting it scrapped. The pointed nose is very much in keeping with the trend of modern supersonic design but that is the only section of the fuselage with any claims to functional beauty.

Roughly halfway along the fuselage there is an immense semi-circular air intake duct on each side and out of these ducts sprout the roots of the wings, a high configuration. The trailing edge of the delta is set about five-sixths of the way along the fuselage and this houses blown flaps for the full width of the wing, apart from the tips. No ailerons are fitted.

The rudder consists of an all-moving fin and the tail unit is an arrangement of pivoted tail-planes which can work in unison as elevators or in opposition as ailerons. This tail unit is set low down below the wing to avoid pitch-up. The undercarriage is more or less conventional, the main wheels retracting into spaces associated with the engine air intakes and the nose wheels rising forward into a space in the fuselage just aft of the rear crew member—the crew is two men, pilot and navigator.

Since at Mach 2+ the aircraft is flying at somewhere near the thermal limits of aluminium alloys it has been necessary to use some specially developed aluminium/lithium alloys which have better characteristics at high temperatures than the conventional aluminium/copper alloys acceptable at lower Mach numbers. In other parts of the airframe use is made of a British titanium alloy which has a strength-to-weight ratio about twice that of heat-resistant steel. A very high quality ultra high tensile steel was specified for use in the undercarriage legs which may have to undergo great stresses when rough ground is used as a landing area. This metal was also developed in Britain.

Much has been said in this book and elsewhere about the effects of high skin temperatures on the materials of supersonic aircraft but usually these comments apply to metals. This is not the whole of the problem, however. A variety of plastics or other non-metal materials have to be used for such components as windscreens, radomes, etc., and these, too, have to be just as heat-resistant as the metallic parts. The British Aircraft Corporation undertook a major programme of research into the behaviour of possible materials in high temperature conditions, a programme which resulted in new types of transparencies being produced.

Resins capable of withstanding high temperatures were

obtained from the United States and even the hydraulic fluid had to be specially prepared to meet the extreme conditions of supersonic operation. Imperial Chemical Industries provided this vital item of equipment as they did the titanium alloy.

It is normal to dissipate some of the friction heat by passing it to the fuel but even this solution was beset by a problem which the layman would overlook. At the start of a flight the tanks would be full, at the end somewhere near empty. So the heat dissipation capacity of the fuel would become progressively less as the flight continued, providing yet another design problem. And the fact that the fuel tanks would be extremely hot meant that the tank sealants would have to stand up to temperatures far higher than would be the case in subsonic aircraft. It also became obvious that a higher standard of mating between metal parts would be needed so as to reduce the work done by the sealants and this in turn called for very accurate machining to close tolerances.

Without attempting to go too deeply into the electronics in the TSR.2, most of which are completely classified and may not be described, it may be said that the navigation system is so complete that it is possible to feed the entire flight plan as a programme into the aircraft's computer and let the aircraft fly itself to its destination, varying height and speed as requisite, discharge its weapons and return home with the crew in the position of passengers, except for take-off and landing. Everything is done to relieve the pilot and navigator of strain but, as they are human beings, they will in practice be working very hard checking the performance of the automatics. And it need hardly be added that the pilot can override the computer at will by either flying the aircraft manually or feeding a new programme into the computer.

In the reconnaissance role the TSR.2, using its multiple radar systems can store its pictures of the area under observation or relay them to base by conventional radio techniques.

All this is only a tithe of the airframe, engine and equipment design problems and innovations but it is enough to explain why the development of the TSR.2 has been an exceptionally expensive business.

An order was placed in October 1960 for nine pre-production aircraft and, two and half years later, this was increased to a total of twenty. The R.A.F. estimated that it would need 140 aircraft in all but permission to order material was given for only 30 production aircraft in March 1964. By this time the cost of the project was the source of many searching questions in Parliament.

The first two aircraft were finally assembled at Boscombe Down, the testing field of the Ministry of Aviation, and the maiden flight, of some 15 minutes duration, was made there on 27 September 1964. Though successful in the sense that the aircraft landed safely, various teething troubles were experienced and it was about three months before the TSR.2 flew again. It was reported that at least one engine change had been made. Since that date up to the time of writing a number of flights have been made but, so far, they have mostly been subsonic. (It must be made clear that this book is being written while the tests go on and, by the time it is published, more information will probably be available.) However, when the first TSR.2 was flown from Boscombe Down to the B.A.C. airfield at Warton, Lancashire, it did exceed sonic speed over the Irish Sea.

Even during the last months of the Conservative government in 1964 there was a great deal of heart-searching going on about the project, purely on account of cost, which seemed to be mounting daily. The Royal Australian Air Force had been at one time interested in the purchase of a large number of TSR.2s but the price frightened them off and they announced their intention of buying the American TFX, an aircraft of comparable but lower performance. It was stated—and not denied officially— that the Ministry of Aviation in Britain had made it a condition of purchase that each aircraft should carry a very considerable portion of the development costs whereas the Americans were prepared to sell their aircraft without this heavy penalty.

Almost immediately the Socialist government took office in Britain in October 1964 it was announced that TSR.2 might be scrapped if an intensive enquiry into its cost did not provide satisfactory answers. By this time it was estimated that perhaps 25,000 people were employed on the work and that all might lose their jobs. It was indicated, though not finally stated, that the order might go to America for the competing TFX. This sparked off a tremendous political row which even brought the trade unions concerned with the aircraft industry out against a government these bodies would normally support whole-heartedly.

A Motion of Censure against the government was tabled by the Opposition to be debated on 2 February 1965. During this debate the Prime Minister announced that—for the time—work would continue on the TSR.2 though another supersonic project, the Hawker Siddeley P.1154 VTOL strike aircraft, would be abandoned. Although the Opposition was defeated on the Vote of Censure, which was not entirely concerned with the aircraft industry, the fact that such a vote was taken at all showed conclusively how important the TSR.2 project was to Britain's economy. Until the whole business was brought out into the open it had not been realised what a tremendous undertaking the production of the TSR.2 really was and how much it affected industries that might have nothing whatsoever to do with aircraft.

Radar techniques were substantially advanced by the demands of terrain-following; metallurgical knowledge advanced further and would confer benefits on any project using alloys that might be subjected to high temperatures; a similar situation existed in connection with plastics; micro-miniaturisation of electronic equipment—and still greater reduction of its weight—moved forward; and knowledge of the behaviour of fuels and lubricants at high temperatures was increased, to mention only a few of the advantages conferred on all and sundry as a result of the need for a special purpose supersonic aircraft.

Rather more space has been devoted to the TSR.2 than would normally be given to just one aircraft in a book of this type because the political disturbances it created brought public realisation on a wide scale that there was more to supersonic flight than just a desire by a few enthusiasts—cranks, according to some commentators—to travel ever faster. Every scientific effort confers some general benefits and supersonic flight is no exception to this rule.

Since writing this chapter the TSR.2 has been scrapped, at the cost of thousands of jobs in the industry. It hardly seems necessary to comment on an action which must harm Britain and benefit America.

11

POWER FOR SUPERSONICS

so far only three types of engine have proved practical for supersonic flight, the turbo-jet, the ram-jet and the rocket. The last has been extensively used in the X-series of experimental aircraft but has—at the time of writing—not been acceptable for commercial or normal military operation. Both pure jets and by-pass (or turbo-fan) engines have been used extensively in supersonic aircraft. The pure jet passes all the air which enters the compressor intake through the combustion chambers and turbines, though some of it is not burnt with the fuel, whereas the by-pass engine bleeds a part of the air round the combustion area and re-combines it with the combustion products behind the turbine wheels. It is claimed that this method produces a quieter engine for a given thrust and that the air bled off assists in cooling the extremely hot areas of the engine.

The choice seems to be a matter of personal taste, however, but one fact does emerge which is more or less equally applicable to both types. A jet engine can operate efficiently at speeds up to about Mach 4.5 but above that it runs into trouble and other forms of propulsion have to be considered. Since Mach 4.5 represents a speed in the region of 3,000 m.p.h. this disability is unlikely to be of serious import until, perhaps, the year 2000. By that time new techniques should be so far advanced that higher speeds will be practicable but in the mid-'sixties the problem is purely academic.

The ram-jet has the tremendous advantage of simplicity being, in effect, just a tube in which air enters at one end, is burnt with fuel and ejected at the far end. The inner shape of the tube provides compression before combustion and a partially closed section ahead of the burner against which the burnt gases produce thrust. This inner shape, so airily dismissed, is very complex and costly to manufacture but the ram-jet has no internal moving parts. It might therefore be considered as the ideal power unit for any aircraft but there is a difficulty inherent in this type of "engine". It can only work if the air entering the intake is already moving fast in relation to the tube or, in other words, it can only function *after* the aircraft has attained a high speed, preferably supersonic. Therefore some other power unit must be provided for initial acceleration and, even though this may be closed down for supersonic cruise or supersonic dash, there is a weight penalty due to this auxiliary engine system. Rolls-Royce, however, has an answer to this problem which will be dealt with later.

Most of the turbo-jet engines of 10,000 lb. static thrust or more have been fitted to one or other of the supersonic aircraft and the problems of one are, roughly speaking, the problems of all. The Rolls-Royce Avon is a representative engine which is in regular use for subsonic airliners and Mach 2 fighters so a brief description of this power unit should tell the story of all engines in this general category. Many variants of this engine have been produced since the first one was type-tested at a thrust of 6,000 lb. in 1948.

A typical Avon engine, of up to 13,000 lb. static thrust, uses an axial flow compressor with 16 or 17 stages, directly coupled to a three-stage axial flow turbine. Eight interconnected combustion chambers are used to burn a high proportion of the air from the final stage of the compressor with fuel, pressure-fed to the burners. The balance of the air is used for cooling purposes and finally mingles with combustion gases ejected through the jet pipe at the rear of the engine. Air from the compressor is also used for anti-icing purposes at the intake end of the engine. This seems like a contradiction but air bled from the compressor is much cooler than, for example, the turbine shaft bearings and much hotter than the air entering the intake at subsonic speeds. The question of icing does not, of course, arise at supersonic speeds as the entire airframe is considerably heated by friction with the air in which it is flying.

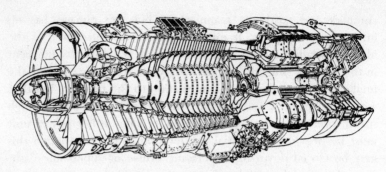

Cutaway of a typical turbo-jet engine

Engines of this type are designed to offer maximum efficiency at high shaft revolutions and it is therefore necessary to allow some adjustment of the air flow through the compressor at other shaft speeds. This is achieved by automatic bleed valves which are open at low speeds and closed progressively as the engine speed rises.

Air from the compressors enters the combustion chambers and passes through swirl vanes round the burner to produce the turbulence needed for efficient burning. The fuel is pressure fed to the burners and ignited, initially, by high energy igniters in two of the flame tubes, the flame passing to the other chambers via the interconnecting tubes. Not all the air enters the chambers at the front end. Some of it passes round the flame tubes in which a number of holes are drilled. Through these holes a part of this air passes and all of it goes through the turbine wheels providing a measure of cooling.

The flame tubes discharge into a nozzle box which is, in fact, an annular gap with access to the whole periphery of the turbine wheel. Guide vanes in the box direct the gases at the best angle on to the turbine blades and the process is repeated for the second and third wheels. Behind the turbine is the jet pipe through which the gases are discharged to the rear and in this pipe is the re-heat burner system.

Much of the air which passes through the engine emerges unburnt and it is this air which is used for re-heat burning. Re-heat, or afterburning as it is called in the U.S.A., is a

method of augmenting thrust by burning fuel with the excess
air in the jet pipe and so providing additional forward pressure
against the turbine casing. It is a form of ram-jet, though rather
an elementary one. At low air speeds this system gives a thrust
augmentation of about 25 per cent but at higher speeds this is
considerably increased. Rolls Royce quote examples for the
Avon engine. At 700 m.p.h. the thrust is increased by 50 per
cent and at 1,000 m.p.h. the figure rises to 65 per cent. And
no greater use of fuel is involved so the value of re-heat at high
air speeds is very great indeed.

Various auxiliaries such as fuel and oil pumps, generators,
etc., are driven through a gear box mounted in the engine and
it is not unusual to use air from the compressor—after suitable
cooling—for cabin pressurisation.

The by-pass engine uses basically the same principle as the
one described for the Avon but there is one essential difference.
It is claimed that greater propulsive efficiency is obtained from
a large mass of air moving at low velocity than from a smaller
mass moving at high velocity. By splitting the compressor into
two sections it is simple to pass some of the air from the first—
or low pressure—compressor into a duct surrounding the rest
of the engine letting it join the combustion gases in the jet
pipe. An additional advantage is gained by this system in that
the air from the low pressure unit assists in cooling the hot
parts of the engine and the actual jet efflux as well. This reduces
the need for elaborate heat shields and makes for a lighter weight
engine. Rolls-Royce tried out this principle for more than ten
years in the Conway by-pass engine fitted to aircraft such as the
V.C.10, Boeing 707 and DC.8 and, from the experience gained,
the firm was able to develop the Spey engine which powers the
Blackburn Buccaneer and may soon be fitted to the McDonnell
Phantoms, Mach 2 strike aircraft, for the Royal Navy. The Spey
is also used in airliners with high subsonic performance such as
the Hawker Siddeley Trident and the B.A.C. 111.

In its essentials the Spey differs from the Avon in having the
by-pass duct and in using two turbines to drive two independent
compressors. This is achieved by linking the two-stage high

pressure turbine to the twelve-stage high pressure compressor by a hollow shaft, and the two-stage low pressure turbine to the four- or five-stage low pressure compressor by a solid shaft running inside the high pressure shaft. This allows the two "spools" to take up speeds ideal to the conditions of running and helps to simplify compressor design. This is not to suggest that these compressors are simple things. They are actually extremely complex and uncountable millions of pounds have gone into their design. The Spey engine will, no doubt, be developed to give higher power in the same way as all the other successful engines have been, but, at the time of writing, the engines have been type tested at a static thrust of 11,400 lb. Compared to the 21,000 lb. of the subsonic Conway or the 13,000 lb. of the Avon this is a low figure but the propulsive efficiency of the engine is very high indeed and the Spey performs more than adequately at Mach 2+.

Among the supersonic aircraft which have been equipped with these Rolls-Royce engines are: the Hawker Hunter (1 Avon), the S.A.A.B. Draken and Lansen (1 Avon each), the Vickers Supermarine Scimitar, the Hawker Siddeley Sea Vixen and the English Electric Lightning (2 Avons each), and the Blackburn (Hawker Siddeley) Buccaneer S.2, and the McDonnell Phantom II (2 Speys each). Not all these aircraft are supersonic in level flight but they all have supersonic capability in the dive.

The higher the mass flow of air into the intake the more power can be developed by a turbo-jet. Purists might point out that there are other factors to be considered but in its essence this simple statement is correct enough. It is therefore a corollary that the colder the air entering the compressor the greater will be its density—and therefore weight. At great heights and at subsonic speeds this ideal is realised but when the speed rises to Mach 1 or above the friction of the air with the airframe and the intake surfaces raises its temperature much higher than is really desirable. Compression of the air further raises the temperature so by the time it reaches the after end of the high pressure compressor the air is very hot indeed. As a result it has become necessary to use metals for the compressor blades and guide vanes which were previously only needed in the turbine section of the engine. These metals, of course, already existed but they are infinitely more expensive than the simple alloys which sufficed at subsonic speeds and that is just another of the many reasons why supersonic aircraft are very costly. The air intake itself is another problem but that is fully discussed in the description of the Bristol Siddeley Olympus engine.

Engines built by other countries, France, America and Russia for example, work on exactly the same principles as the British ones so the Rolls-Royce and Bristol products discussed here may be taken as representative of the world's output of supersonic engines. Space has not, therefore, been given to descriptions of any engines other than the British ones but it may be said authoritatively that the products of other countries are similar in efficiency to those produced in the United Kingdom. National pride does, however, come into this matter because it is an admitted fact that Britain has led in jet engine development.

In this connection it is also a fact that whereas the engine for the Anglo-French Concord has already been chosen no final selection has yet been made for the American SST. It lies between Pratt and Whitney and the American General Electric Company, both of which firms have produced many thousands of successful engines. The principal difference between the British and American engines seems to be in the fact that the Concord is scheduled for Mach 2.2 and the American aircraft Mach 3. This means a considerable increase of temperature at the intake and, of course, some difference in the geometry of the intake to deal with the different shock wave conditions at the higher speed. By the time this book is published it is possible the choice will have been made, but the whole situation is very much in the melting pot as these words are written.

Bristol-Siddeley engines are just as famous as Rolls-Royce though it must be admitted that, in recent years, there have been more Rolls-Royce engines installed in civil aircraft and it might therefore be deduced that Bristol has had less practical experience with supersonic flying. However, the two rivals have both had their ups and downs and they might currently be said to be running neck and neck. The selection of the Bristol Olympus for both the TSR.2 and the Concord will just about balance accounts.

As the Concord airframe is a joint Anglo-French effort so are the engines. Bristol-Siddeley can certainly claim to be responsible for all the basic work on the Olympus but they have joined forces with the Société Nationale d'Etude et de Construction de Moteurs d'Aviation, more conveniently known by the unpleasant-sounding name of SNECMA. This French company has been responsible for designing and producing the magnificent Atar series of turbo-jets which have powered a number of French military aircraft in the supersonic range such as the Mirage series. SNECMA has specialised in re-heat systems, variable area nozzles and thrust reversers and the knowledge thus acquired has done much to make the already good Olympus a still better engine.

Like the Rolls-Royce products, the Olympus engine has been developed almost out of all recognition from the original engine of 9,000 lb. static thrust. This one first ran on the bench as long ago as May 1950. Various marks of the engine have powered the Vulcan V-bombers and the thrust has steadily increased until the Vulcan Mark 2 aircraft are fitted with engines of 17,000 lb. thrust without re-heat. Development did not stop there. The Olympus Mark 301 was type-tested in February 1962 at 20,000 lb. thrust and from that engine has followed the military 22R which powers the TSR.2. It has not been disclosed what thrust is available from this engine but it may reasonably be guessed that it exceeds 30,000 lb. because the Olympus 593, a comparable engine, will start life in the Concord at 32,500 lb., without re-heat.

A civil engine meets more exacting demands in some respects than does a military engine. It is true that combat conditions may call for longer periods at maximum thrust but, if an emergency should arise the crew has the opportunity to eject. No such freedom exists for the crew and passengers of an airliner. A good example of a civil emergency would be failure of the pressurising system, unlikely perhaps but not impossible. In this event a descent to below 10,000 feet might be needed and the aircraft would then be forced to continue its flight at subsonic speed, possibly for several hours. Failure of one or two of the four engines could produce a similar condition. So the civil engine has to be capable of prolonged periods of running in abnormal conditions in addition to the standard demands, which are not too easy to meet. These conditions cover take-off, subsonic climb, transonic acceleration, supersonic cruise, subsonic descent and subsonic stand-off and the engine must have maximum possible efficiency in all of them.

Clearly, the selected engine must be a compromise but there is an additional problem. The optimum engine must be the lightest engine giving the required performance and it must not exceed the take-off noise limitations. The various design authorities chose the civil derivative of the Olympus 22R as being the nearest approach to the virtually impossible ideal demanded and this engine benefited from using components already proven in thousands of hours of Vulcan flight. It was also expected that it would benefit from the test phases of the TSR.2 but the doubts about continuation with this strike aircraft left this aspect of 593 test in a rather uncertain state.

The engines are mounted in pairs—but as separate units— outboard of the main undercarriage and under the wings at about mid-semi-span. The intakes are in positions where they are sheltered under the wing, which acts as a flow straightener and minimises the effect of the angle of attack on the intake performance.

The air intakes are built by the airframe manufacturers, being more akin to their work than that of engine builders, but they are an integral part of the engine and are therefore described here.

The function of the intake is to provide a *subsonic* air flow into the engine during all conditions of flight.

To ensure that optimum pressure recovery and air mass flow are obtainable, each engine has its own individual air intake which is rectangular and of variable geometry to maintain intake efficiency throughout the speed range. This is achieved by incorporating a variable-angle ramp in the upper surface of the

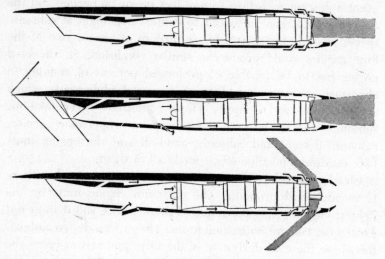

The air intake and jet pipe for the Concord

intake throat. Two movable parts, hinged together and mounted at the front and rear ends, may be raised or lowered to suit the throat area requirements according to the aircraft Mach number. In addition to altering the throat area the variable ramp adjusts the pattern of the shock waves by which compression of the air is achieved in the mouth of the intake at supersonic speeds. This compression has to be as efficient as possible and it is essential that transient changes, either in ambient conditions or engine behaviour, should not upset the shock pattern.

A rapid acting spill vent is situated in the diffuser of the air intake to spill varying quantities of air during supersonic flight in order to balance any difference between the air mass flow supplied by the intake and that required by the engine.

When the engine is throttled back the amount of air required is reduced but it is important to ensure that no spillage of excess air occurs over the intake lip. If it does there is a heavy drag penalty and it may cause an unstable air flow condition, known as "buzz", which can result in severe damage to the intake and, in the extreme case, to the airframe itself. This is another of the problems inherent in supersonic flight which costs time and money to solve. The solution in this case is a relatively simple one; an auxiliary dump door is provided in the lower intake surface which, when open, allows excess air inside the intake to flow away to atmosphere. It is, in effect, a coarse control with the spill vent providing fine control.

The design of the intake diffuser duct involves a change in cross-sectional shape from rectangular to circular. This change could result in a build-up of boundary layer air which would affect the smooth flow of air into the compressor. To prevent this the intake is converged in front of the engine and this accelerates the flow. The spill vent also serves to remove boundary layer air from the after end of the intake.

It is very important that only free-stream air shall enter the intake and this consideration has affected the position of the intake entry. Even so, there is the matter of boundary layer air beneath the wing surface. This is removed by providing a duct between the intake upper leading edge and the wing surface. The considerable quantity of air which finds its way into this duct is led to an annular duct surrounding the jet pipe and becomes a secondary airflow surrounding the primary variable nozzle. There is a faint resemblance to a by-pass engine in this arrangement.

The engine itself is basically similar to other turbo-jets except that it is larger and it is, incidentally, the first civil engine designed for supersonic flying. The two-spool system is used with high temperature blades and guide vanes in the compressors. Air entering the low pressure compressor is already at 150° C. Cooled stator and rotor blades are fitted to the turbines and they run cooler than most uncooled turbines in spite of the fact that the gas temperatures are considerably higher than could be tolerated by uncooled blades. Eight flame tubes feeding into an annular duct are provided.

The exhaust system comprises a jet pipe, a fully variable primary nozzle, which can incorporate re-heat and silencing, and a secondary divergent nozzle and thrust reverser. The jet pipe is attached to the engine by an easily detached articulated joint and flexible bellows which maintain a gas- and fuel-tight joint and allow for independent expansion of both the engine and jet pipe.

Cooling of the jet pipe surface is effected by passing the wing boundary air from the intake bleed over its skin; this air then flows from the annulus surrounding the primary nozzle into the divergent secondary nozzle, where it is used to maintain stable flow through, and discharge from, the secondary nozzle. This cushion of air reduces the need for perfectly profiled surfaces and enables good performance to be obtained over a wide range of flow conditions.

It is expected that transonic acceleration will take place at between 36,000 and 45,000 feet and, if necessary for reasons of sonic boom, the required thrust may be obtained by means of limited re-heat with a temperature of about 1,300° K. It seems unlikely that the re-heat system will be necessary when the Olympus thrust has been developed to 35,000 lb.—as it will be before the Concord goes into service—but if it is installed it will be of the single-gutter type with a horizontal gutter containing the fuel injectors mounted transversally across the primary nozzle and fairly near to the low pressure turbine.

The function of the nozzle system is to convert the thermal and pressure energy of the engine gas stream into kinetic energy and hence thrust. The nozzle design had to be a compromise between the requirements of supersonic cruise operation at high pressure ratios (about 15 to 1) where the bulk of the expansion is carried out in the divergent section of the nozzle, and of subsonic operation with a pressure ratio of the order of 2 or 3 to 1. In this condition a simple convergent nozzle would be adequate.

During subsonic operation at low pressure ratio it is necessary not only to close down the final nozzle area but also to fill in a large proportion of the remaining base area with secondary air. The intake boundary flow is not sufficient for this purpose and it is augmented by nacelle boundary layer air taken in through auxiliary doors.

In the supersonic condition the final nozzle is matched so that the jet is fully expanded and there is very little external drag due to "boat-tailing" of the rear end of the nacelle. The secondary flow is taken from the intake boundary layer bleed and is used for engine bay ventilation as well as providing an aerodynamic cushion over which the main jet expands. The auxiliary doors are, of course, closed in this phase of operation. The secondary flow also provides a degree of cooling for the structure surrounding the engine and jet pipe.

An additional function of the secondary nozzle is to provide reverse thrust during the landing run. Two small buckets are closed across the gas stream after it has passed through the primary nozzle, thus deflecting the gas flow on to cascades which are housed in the top and bottom surfaces of the nacelle. These cascades reverse the flow direction and so provide reverse thrust. As always with reverse thrust or reverse pitch propeller systems there is an interlock which prevents airborne operation.

The distribution of effort in the design and construction of these engines for the Concord is as follows. Bristol-Siddeley is responsible for the intake design and for the engine itself. B.A.C. is building the engine nacelles and intakes and SNECMA has designed—and will build—the variable area nozzles, re-heat installations and thrust reversers.

Engine testing—on the bench—began at Bristol in July 1964 and, slightly earlier, tests began with the variable nozzles at SNECMA's Melun-Villaroche establishment in France. On the current situation the work on the engine sections of the Concord is running a little ahead of schedule. It must naturally be assumed that some difficulties will arise—they always do in any new project—but the time margin gained so far should give the manufacturers a good chance to be ready for test flying when the airframes are complete. This book will, of course, be published before the Concord prototype flies for the first time and it is therefore dangerous to prophesy too rigidly. It can only be said that in the autumn of 1965 the position looks very satisfactory.

In view of the comments made earlier about the relative lightness of the by-pass engine compared to the pure turbo-jet it is reasonable to ask why this type of engine was not chosen for the Concord. Bristol-Siddeley gave the answer in the following terms. "The turbo-jet cycle was selected for the Concord as a result of two primary considerations: first, overall powerplant efficiency, and second, total powerplant weight considerations. The turbo-jet can be shown to give very near to optimum specific fuel consumption at the Concord supersonic cruise condition. Any small advantage which the turbo-fan (by-pass) engine might have over the turbo-jet will be more than offset by the increased powerplant weight and drag resulting from the larger intake, diffuser and exhaust system needed to accommodate the fan airflow. These penalties are such that, if fan engines were to be fitted to the present aircraft with the same payload, maximum all-up weight would be exceeded by 5 per cent, or alternatively, the payload would have to be reduced by about ten passengers."

It was mentioned earlier in this chapter that the ram-jet had great possibilities for flight at very high Mach numbers but that a weight penalty existed because some other powerplant was needed to accelerate the aircraft to a speed at which the ram-jet could generate thrust, something it is incapable of doing in a static condition. Rolls-Royce offers a partial solution to this problem with a "turbo-ram-jet".

Essentially this consists of a by-pass engine with re-heat but there are differences. The by-pass is used to get the aircraft off the ground and accelerate it to a suitable speed. The re-heat may or may not be in use during this acceleration phase but when the required speed is attained the by-pass engine is shut down, doors in the intake divert almost all the incoming air into the by-pass duct and the re-heat burners then take over. There is, of course, a considerable amount of deadweight to be carried under ram-jet conditions but some advantage is gained in this respect and the idea has the merit of simplicity. However, it is currently no more than an idea which may or may not be tried out in practice.

There is another British engine which was designed specifically for supersonic operation, the de Havilland (now Bristol-Siddeley) Gyron Junior. This engine was a scaled down version of the Gyron and first ran on the test bed in August 1955. It was intended to provide a thrust, with re-heat, of 20,000 lb. at speeds above Mach 2.5 at 36,000 feet and, in a decompression chamber, combined with a wind tunnel, attained this performance. A pure turbo-jet, the Gyron Junior was fitted to the Bristol T.188 research aircraft and performed moderately successfully but the test programme of this machine was somewhat curtailed and the engine more or less faded out of the picture. It was test flown for some considerable time in a Gloster Javelin. The amalgamation of de Havilland Engines with Bristol finally resulted in the Olympus being chosen as the engine most suited to further development but it would be unfair to overlook the Gyron Junior altogether.

Engines need fuel and, on the face of it, this is only a problem for the SST engines insofar as they burn more fuel and the aircraft therefore has to lift a greater weight of it off the ground. Unfortunately, it is not quite so simple as that. The heat generated by the passage of the aircraft through the air has a number of direct and some indirect effects on the fuel, both in the storage tanks and in actual burning.

It was already well-known, long before supersonic flight was considered, that fuels, both of the petrol and paraffin types, were liable to deposit varnishes, etc., on tanks, pipes and filters if they were subjected to very high temperatures. Another factor was the danger of spontaneous ignition at high temperatures unless certain precautions, such as inhibiting with nitrogen or other inert gases, were taken in the fuel system of an aeroplane. With subsonic aircraft these facts, though important, presented no serious difficulties and, indeed, it has been normal practice for many years now to pass the fuel for jet engines through a heat exchanger to cool the lubricating oil. This took place just before the fuel entered the burners and had no deleterious effect on the thrust developed.

With supersonic aircraft, however, the position is very different. The aircraft will fly at supersonic cruise conditions bathed in a layer of hot air, varying from 120° C. in the case of the Mach 2.2 Concord to about 300° C. for the American SST. Some estimates are even higher, Bristol-Siddeley taking the view that the layer of hot air will be at nearer 150° C. for the slower aircraft. This is a minor difference but it gives some idea of the vessel in which the fuel has to be carried. It is further estimated that the fuel in the tanks, which will be at least partially insulated from the outside skin, will settle down to a basic temperature of 80° C. The plan, therefore, is to use the stored fuel as a heat sink to cool the air fed through the pressurising system into the cabin and, according to Dr. S. G. Hooker, technical director of Bristol-Siddeley, this will raise the storage temperature of the Concord fuel to 143° C. Comparable figures are not available for the American aircraft but it is a safe assumption that if the same system is used—and it seems that it must be for reasons which will follow—the stored fuel temperature can hardly be lower than 200°C. This may seem a frightening prospect for the passengers but anyone who has visited an oil refinery will know that highly inflammable liquids and gases are treated at much higher temperatures than this and that fires virtually never happen.

It had been considered that it might be practicable to install refrigerating plant to cool the cabin air and the fuel but, though the weight penalty was perhaps acceptable, the increase in drag was estimated to be at least 10 per cent. That would result in a lower speed or, with the use of greater power, the same speed could be obtained by burning more fuel. And that would immediately introduce a further weight penalty in the form of heavier engines as well as greater weight of fuel and tankage. Pre-refrigeration, too, proved far too costly so artificial cooling of the fuel could not be accepted.

A huge testing programme was undertaken by the principal producers of aviation fuels using a device already invented to check the thermal stability of turbine fuels, the Fuel Coker. This installation judges fuel quality on the basis of qualitative examination of the deposits formed on the outer surface of a tube forming part of a heat exchanger and of the increase in pressure drop across a sintered metal filter caused by the trapping of fuel insolubles. Results obtained this way have fitted in very exactly with the actual conditions found in aircraft engines using these fuels, the heat exchanger deposits relating to the accumulation of gummy deposits and lacquers found in the fuel manifolds of the engines themselves and the filter deposits to the blockage of atomisers and their protective filters.

From these tests it appeared, originally, that the standard subsonic jet fuels were unlikely to prove satisfactory for use at the temperatures induced by Mach 3 operation because material degradation of the fuel would occur with long periods of exposure to the temperatures expected. It was also feared that the reserve fuel, which might amount to 15 per cent of the total and therefore a very large number of gallons, would be so degraded by the end of a flight that it would be unsuitable for mixing with fresh fuel and would make a big increase in operating costs. Luckily, this fear proved to be unfounded but the question of thermal stability was still a worrying one—for Mach 3 temperatures.

The Mach 2.2 case, however, is much better and this perhaps provides one of the strongest arguments in favour of the lower speed aircraft, at least until a great deal of further development work has been done with aviation paraffins. Dr. Hooker stated that experiments had shown that the standard JP1 fuel used for subsonic engines remained completely stable up to temperatures of 200° C. and could therefore be used with certainty in the Concord where, after using the fuel as a heat sink for the aircraft as well as for cooling the engine oil, the temperature of entry to the burners would be 171° C.

This matter of fuel heat is far from being the only problem in Mach 3 airliner operation but it is a very important one and it may throw some light on why the Americans have been beset with design difficulties both for the SST and the B.70 bomber which has proved to be such a ghastly fiasco after an estimated $1,300 million have been spent on its development.

It might be assumed that lubricants also suffer from the same snags but in fact this is not so. Jet engines already run so hot that special synthetic lubricants have been developed which do the work adequately though they have a relatively short life. The engine temperatures in the Olympus are certainly higher than in other engines but such adequate cooling arrangements have been included that the oil can do its work successfully. It is normal to think of lubrication in terms of the car engine with its multiplicity of reciprocating parts but, though the gas turbine runs faster and hotter, the motion is all pure rotation without change of direction and lubrication is somewhat easier. And there are no sliding friction surfaces as there are when a piston moves up and down in a cylinder. So, though immense sums have been spent in producing adequate lubricants, at least this problem does not bristle with as many difficulties as the fuel one does.

12

SUPERSONIC AIRLINER DESIGN FACTORS

AS has already been explained, aerodynamic designs best suited to slow flight are not necessarily ideal, or even practicable, for high speed flight. As speeds have increased a change has taken place from the straight wing, that is, projecting at right angles to the fuselage, to the swept wing with its leading edge making only a small angle with the fore and aft line through the fuselage. From that phase to the triangular wing, or the true delta, was only a small modification and this is the pattern of most supersonic aircraft in current use in the mid-1960s.

In general terms it can be said that the delta wing is ideal for very high speed flying but not too good for slow speeds such as are involved in landing and take-off. The straight wing, on the other hand, is good for slow flying but quite inappropriate if efficiency at high speed is called for. As always in engineering design there has to be compromise and present trends show that the delta wing can be modified so as to be reasonably efficient at low speeds and to give great efficiency at the high speeds at which an aircraft will fly for most of its airborne time. However, there is an alternative, variable geometry, which it is claimed can offer the best of both worlds.

This is not a new idea, in fact, it is one of the oldest in the history of man's attempts to fly. The flapping wing of the bird is an example of almost infinite variable geometry and the early ornithopters made use of this principle—with uniform lack of success. More recently various projects have been put forward to allow wings to fold back under controlled conditions in flight to give the slow flying advantages of the straight wing and the high speed advantages of the swept wing. Not many of these designs ever went beyond the sketch-on-the-back-of-an-envelope stage but there is one marked exception to this state-

ment. Dr. B. N. Wallis, better known as Barnes Wallis of the
Dam Busters era, designed a variable geometry airframe which
became known as the "Swallow". This design was intended to
be used for an airliner capable of reaching Mach 5, about 3,000
m.p.h., and a flying model was built which worked extremely
well. It included what would now be regarded as a most unpractical arrangement of the engines, these being mounted in
vertical pairs on the wing tips and arranged to swing so that
they always faced ahead as the wings were folded back from the
straight to something akin to the delta configuration.

Now, of course, it would be accepted that the engines could
be tail-mounted but in every other respect this design, which is
around ten years old at a time when supersonic airliner design
is far from finalised, has many of the characteristics included in
the Boeing variable geometry project.

The case for variable geometry as put forward by Boeing is,
in simple terms, that the complications and weight of the
equipment needed to move—and lock—the wings are more
than counteracted by the improvement in aerodynamic efficiency
throughout the entire speed range of a supersonic aircraft.
It is also stressed that there need be no fear that this equipment
could go wrong and cause a disaster. In the unlikely event that
the wing-moving gear failed while the wings were in the low
speed position the aircraft would just not go supersonic and
could return to base in perfect safety. On the other hand, if a
failure occurred under supersonic conditions and the wings
could not be brought forward to the approach and landing
position the only disadvantage would be that the landing would
have to be made at a higher speed than normal but not at a speed
too high for the runways available on airports that would be
used by supersonic transports.

A third possibility may occur to the exceptionally nervous
passenger; that the wings might become loose and flap backwards
and forwards uncontrollably. As the gear is designed on the
"fail-safe" principle this just could not happen, a simple
analogy being the arrangement on railway signals where a break

in the operating cables or rods results in the counterweight bringing the signal to the "danger" position automatically.

Variable geometry is not limited to changing the sweep of the wings. There are proposals for major changes in the configuration of the tail unit and for a movable windscreen to reduce drag at high speeds. And it must be remembered that conventional aircraft already have a large amount of variable geometry which is accepted as normal. Elevators, ailerons, rudder, trailing and leading edge flaps, retractable undercarriages and tailwheels or nosewheels, retractable radomes, even retractable aerials are already commonplace so it is not unreasonable to carry the process a step further.

The Boeing idea is to vary the wing sweep so as to match the movement aft of the aerodynamic centre of the aircraft as it goes through the transonic range and to make the fullest use of leading and trailing edge flaps so as to simulate the thicker wing appropriate to low speed flying while retaining the thin section wing which is required for efficient high speed flight. There was also consideration of the movable windshield which is claimed to give a drag reduction of nearly fifty per cent for that part of the fuselage at the transonic and supersonic stages of flight, but this was not proceeded with. Air brakes are now common additions to high speed aircraft and these too would be included in the variable geometry of the Boeing aircraft intended to cruise at about 1,800 m.p.h.

Even this catalogue does not complete the movable parts of the aircraft. The air intake to the jet engines is greatly affected by the speed and height of the flight. At low altitudes the air is relatively dense and warm and it enters the compressors at low speed. At supersonic speed and altitude the air is much thinner and colder but it is entering the compressors at a much greater rate. It is true that to some extent these factors balance each other in that the higher rate of airflow is needed at the higher speeds as more fuel is burnt and therefore more air is needed for efficient combustion. Unfortunately, the problem is not as simple as that because air temperature affects its density and therefore the mass flow, and certain heating effects take place in the intake due to surface friction, similar to those as the air passes over the wings and the fuselage.

It is therefore necessary to devise certain variables in the shape of the intake system so as to balance the air flow with the needs of the engine and this involves bleeding some of the air away from the compressors and using it for other purposes such as cabin pressurisation, cooling the turbine wheels and so on. Much of this variable geometry is automatically operated by the current setting of the engine controls, the altitude and the Mach number at which the aircraft is flying. In addition, the actual physical shape of the intake duct is altered to meet the varying conditions of flight.

This last item is common to the conventional delta aircraft with fixed wings and to the Boeing design with variable sweep.

The Boeing supersonic airliner, as presented to the American Federal Aviation Authority, has these characteristics. The wing sweep is at 20° for take-off and climb to transonic altitude—generally about 40,000 feet—for the transonic stage it will move back to 42° and for supersonic cruise the full sweepback of 74° will be used. The company claims that with this configuration a twenty-five per cent reduction of engine power can be achieved compared with that needed by a conventional delta shape aircraft with resultant decrease of airfield noise and community noise during the initial climb to transonic altitude.

This aircraft, which is at present designated as the Boeing 733, is planned for a gross weight of 430,000 lb. and a wing span, at 20° sweepback, of 173 feet 4 inches, reducing to 86 feet 4 inches with full sweepback. The tail fin will have a height of 48 feet 4 inches above the ground. The basic design length is quoted as 203 feet 10 inches but there is provision for extending the fuselage by a further 45 feet for intercontinental operation thereby increasing the passenger capacity from its basic 150 to 227 and the gross weight to 520,000 lb. The fuel capacity for a range exceeding 4,000 statute miles is 35,000 U.S. gallons.

The engines will be mounted in pods beneath the fixed section of the wing and not in or under the tail as is now visualised for the delta-type airliners. This arrangement is in conformity with

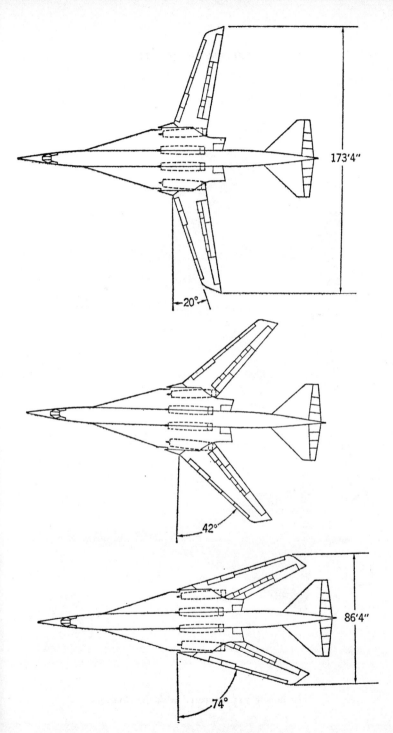

173'4"

20°

42°

86'4"

74°

The Boeing 733 in different sweep conditions

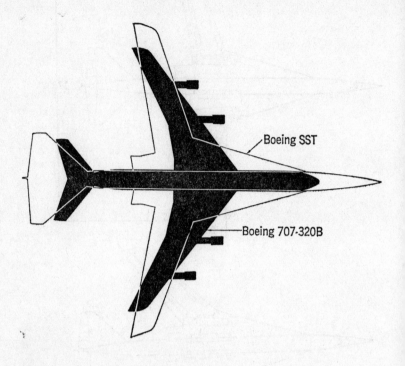

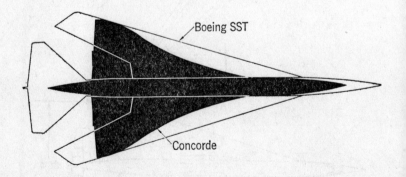

The Boeing 733 compared with the Concord

Boeing practice so extensively proved with their subsonic civil and military aircraft.

Comparison between the shape of the Boeing 733 at take-off and the subsonic Boeing 707 in the accompanying drawing shows that the sweepback is less in the 733 than in the subsonic aircraft while, in the other picture, with the wings fully swept, the similarity between the 733 and the Concord is very marked.

Apart from the variable sweep the 733 is planned to be more or less conventional in design. The tail is of the fixed variety, as is the windscreen and all flying controls will follow proved existing methods with the exception of the trailing and leading edge flaps. It will be obvious that these could not be used when the wings are fully swept so the control of sweep and flap position has been combined in one lever as illustrated. The flaps cannot be lowered until the sweep control has brought the wings back to 20°. After that continued movement of the lever lowers the flaps in a conventional way.

The wing pivot bearing is the king pin of the whole design

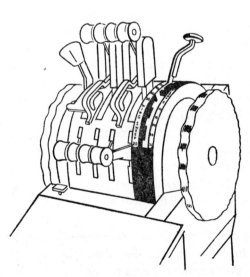

Boeing 733 wing sweep control

and, like most good examples of engineering practice, it is completely simple. Having a dual load path it is of a shape and size which allows complete inspection without dismantling. The bearing is 36 inches in diameter and the inner hole is 21 inches in diameter, allowing a man to get inside. It is also designed so that either bearing can be replaced without removing or even jigging the wing. The bearing life has been planned for at least 10,000 complete sweep cycles and, in parenthesis, since the aircraft is expected to make non-stop flights of about 3,500 miles, this would mean a flying life of 35,000,000 miles between bearing changes.

Consideration has obviously been given to the possibility of abnormal conditions building up at or beyond the half-way point an intercontinental flight. The chart shows that even if failures occurred so severe as to cause the aircraft to fly subsonic on only two engines it would be able to complete its mission. And the loss of one engine would not prevent the flight being completed in the supersonic condition. These safety margins would appear to satisfy not only the licensing authorities of all nations but also the most critical opponents of the whole concept. Only in the extreme case of the cabin pressure being lost and the flight continued at low altitude and subsonic speed would it be impossible to reach the planned destination but ample reserve would exist to complete the Atlantic crossing and get into any one of a number of alternates.

The case as presented by Boeing for the variable geometry aircraft is a very convincing one with the positive claim that initial cost and direct operating cost will both be lower than for the conventional delta. This claim is, of course, matched by a similar one in favour of the other aircraft but, as none of them has yet been built and therefore not subjected to a practical cost analysis, the accuracy of the claims will not be assessed for several years.

Very little has been said by Boeing about the structural materials to be used, very little in detail, that is. But it was stated at an early press conference that titanium would be used as a basic material and, in support of this, it was pointed out that the

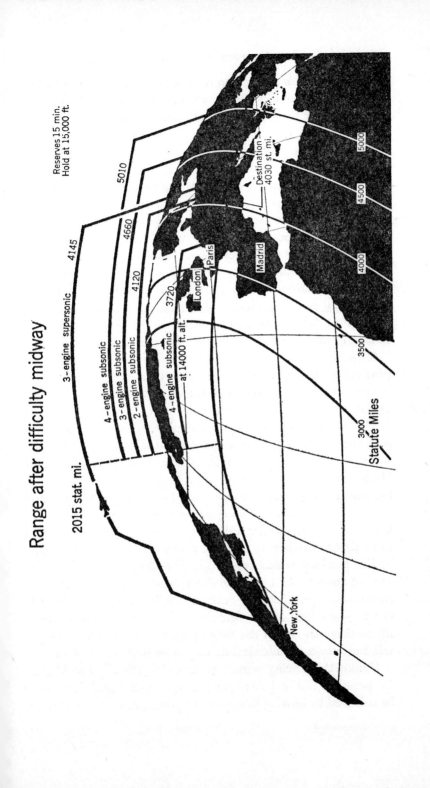

Range after difficulty midway

Reserves 15 min.
Hold at 15,000 ft.

2015 stat. mi.

5010

4660

4145   3-engine supersonic

4120

3720

4-engine subsonic
3-engine subsonic
2-engine subsonic

4-engine subsonic
at 14000 ft. alt.

London
Paris

Madrid

Destination
4030 st. mi.

5000

4500

4000

3500

3000

Statute Miles

New York

company had been engaged on research and actual use of titanium for more than sixteen years. During this time techniques to produce heavy forgings and sheets had been evolved and every normal method of machining the metal had been successfully employed. Heat treating, stress relieving and cleaning procedures had been developed and were already in regular use. Boeing had built sample wing spars, panels and trailing edges, a complete wing section with integral fuel tanks, a fuselage section with windows and various undercarriage parts. These have all undergone extensive test procedures and appeared to meet the demands of the designers. Test specimens, at the time of writing, are undergoing a 30,000 hour test under supersonic operating conditions, that is, they are subjected to various mechanical stresses while maintained at a temperature of 300° C. or taken rapidly from well below freezing point to this temperature and then returned to a very cold state again.

It can safely be stated that never before has so severe a test programme been applied to an aeroplane before it has been built and this applies equally to the other American designs and to the Anglo-French Concord.

The planned life of any accepted supersonic transport is between 30,000 and 40,000 hours. In the Mach 2.2 case this would translate into a minimum mileage of 60 million and in the Mach 3 design the maximum would be 120 million. During that life one Boeing aircraft would carry—assuming a 65 per cent load factor—about 2½ million passengers across the Atlantic. The Concord, with its smaller seating capacity and lower speed, might carry about one-third to half that number in the same flying life.

The thinking which resulted in the design of the Concord and, of course, the Lockheed delta, was based on similar considerations, i.e. that the rearward shift of the aerodynamic centre—or centre of lift—and its resultant effect on the ratio of lift to drag was one of the major problems to be overcome if a safe and easy-to-handle aircraft was to be built.

Unlike the Boeing school of thought, the British Aircraft Corporation and Sud Aviation considered that this shift could be balanced by moving the centre of gravity in a simple manner.

All they considered necessary would be a means of shifting part of the fuel load to a trim tank in the extreme tail of the aircraft and tests showed that this method was feasible—and safe.

They also found that by modifying the shape of the delta wing and giving increased sweepback at the root and the tip greatly improved slow flying characteristics could be achieved. By rounding the tip and extending the root fillet forward it was found possible to maintain the leading edge vortex sheet down to and below the stall condition. At minimum control speed this vortex increases lift by up to 30 per cent in free air but when the ground cushion effect is present the increase in lift is twice as much. Thus a variable area wing is simulated with no mechanical problems and though it would not be claimed that this design gives quite the flexibility of the variable sweep wing it does go a long way to overcome the relative inefficiency of the delta wing at low speed.

Having decided that the modified delta configuration could offer the basis for an aircraft of adequate subsonic and supersonic range the next question that had to be settled was that of maximum cruise speed. Clearly it had to be above Mach 1.2 as this is, roughly, the upper limit of the transonic phase with its attendant control problems. Up to Mach 2.2 some existing aluminium alloys would be acceptable as far as their susceptibility to temperature changes was concerned but at Mach 3 this would no longer be true and other metals would have to be introduced, raising manufacturing costs and injecting many new factors of behaviour about which less was known.

It was also true, as Sir George Edwards put it in a lecture to the Institute of Transport early in 1964, that "We know a lot about aircraft designed for Mach 2 but nothing about Mach 3. This may be an old-fashioned reason for choosing Mach 2 but those responsible for the success of a great undertaking are always likely to be less adventurous than the enthusiastic supporter. As a result it was concluded that the best design speed was likely to be Mach 2.2 where the general kinetic temperature of 120° C. could be tolerated by available light alloys with only a minimum use of steel and titanium."

BAC and Sud also differed from the American line of thought in the matter of size. The Americans took the view that about 200 passengers should be carried—at Mach 3—whereas the European consortium planned for about 100—at the lower speed. There were several considerations involved in this choice. First perhaps was the question of sonic boom. A larger aircraft would, in rather a sweeping generalisation, make a bigger bang and it would therefore have to climb higher, perhaps 10,000 feet higher, before going supersonic than would the 100-seater. Next, the greater the weight the greater the power needed to lift the aircraft and, as a natural corollary, the more fuel would be burnt. These two factors alone would have compelled attention but the availability of traffic also entered the overall equation.

On the reasonable assumption that each Concord would be air-borne for not less than 3,000 hours in a year one aircraft would be able to make more than 1,000 Atlantic crossings annually. Economically it would be desirable that not less than 65 passengers should be carried per flight—ideally, of course, a much higher load factor is looked for—and that would mean that one aircraft would carry 65,000 passengers, absolute minimum, per year.

In 1963, Atlantic passenger traffic totalled about $2\frac{1}{2}$ million passengers and extrapolation of the rate of traffic increase suggested that the figure would reach about 6,500,000 by 1973 when the Concord should have been in service for something over a year. Such a long look ahead can only be classed as intelligent guess-work and the market research experts have already been proved very wrong indeed on a previous occasion in respect to Atlantic air traffic. However, on the basis that this steady ten per cent—or more—traffic rise does take place for ten years the total traffic could be carried in 100 Concords operating at a 65 per cent load factor. If the load factor rose near to 100 per cent the aircraft requirement would be materially less.

If the American view that 200-seat aircraft are needed were to be accepted only fifty supersonic transports would be required

Above, the Lockheed YF.12A. This mach 3 American military strike aircraft was the first production aircraft to have a cruising speed of 2,000 mph and holds the world's speed record of 2,062 mph; *below*, 1,500 mph CF-104s of the RCAF at an air defence demonstration in Western Germany

Left, the Bristol-Siddeley/SNECMA Olympus 593 engine is to be used in the Concord; *below*, a Spey by-pass jet being prepared for test running in the Rolls-Royce altitude test facility at Derby. A military version of the engine has been developed to power the Blackburn Buccaneer S.2 strike aircraft

but this could not satisfy the needs of all the operators working on the North Atlantic. And no airline working as a national flag carrier could afford to be out of this intensely competitive race, so, as happened when the big subsonic jets first came on the scene, load factors would be reduced to ridiculous—and financially crippling—figures. To carry this to its logical conclusion it has to be acknowledged that by the time the supersonic airliners have run out their useful lives in the mid-1980's the traffic may well have grown large enough to justify the bigger aircraft but the operators might have such huge deficits that they could only stay in business by the courtesy of their national taxpayers. That, at all events, is the opinion of many authorities who have studied the traffic patterns with the utmost care. They may be wrong but this type of thinking has been partly reflected in the European decision to go ahead with a 100-seat design. The view of the manufacturers—naturally, a different one—is covered fully in Chapter 13.

The Concord, therefore, has been evolved from two nearly identical designs, the Sud Aviation Super-Caravelle and the

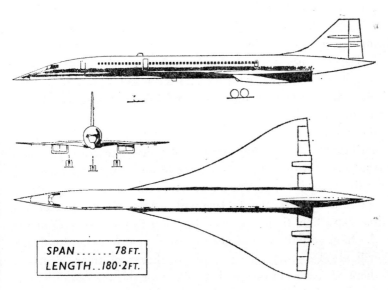

SPAN .... 78 FT.
LENGTH .. 180·2 FT.

Concord: general arrangement

Bristol 223, with an all-up weight of approximately 326,000 lb.

The power plant for the aircraft will be housed in compartments integrated with the after ends of the wings, close inboard to the fuselage and slung below the wing. Control will be by conventional rudder and by elevons, six in number. On each trailing edge there will be one elevon inboard of the engines and two outboard.

The slender delta shape has high inertia to pitch and yaw but low inertia in roll, so co-ordination will be built in between elevator and rudder action to deal with the problem of cross-wind landings. Actuation of the control surfaces will be by hydraulic jacks controlled by a duplicated electrical signalling system but a separate stand-by mechanical system with hydraulic servo assistance is to be provided to allow for total electrical failure.

Provision is being made to droop the flight deck section of the Concord during landing and this will be the only non-conventional piece of variable geometry in the aircraft. As in all deltas the approach is made with the nose held very high and it is considered possible that, at the moment of touch-down, the pilot's eyes may be 50 feet above the runway with all view of the ground cut off. Hence the "droop-snoot" as this feature has been inelegantly named.

The thermal problem has already been discussed at some length but there is a factor which has not so far been mentioned, one which affects all supersonic airliners, irrespective of wing or fuselage shape. To maintain crew and passenger comfort the cabin temperature must be held somewhere between 18.3° and 26.7° C. according to national preference but the skin of the aircraft will be at 120° C. in the Mach 2.2 case and at 300° C. in the Mach 3 design. The expansion of the outside of the aircraft and, in particular, the fuselage will therefore be far greater than the expansion of the inner cabin. Even in the cooler Concord, the fuselage will be 9 inches longer in supersonic cruise than it will on the ground in average weather conditions. Provision therefore has had to be made to allow for this marked difference in physical size between the inside and outside of the fuselage and some very pretty anchoring methods have been evolved to prevent the whole aircraft tearing itself to pieces as it flies.

Not quite so serious a problem but one which has caused some thought is the fact that certain parts of the skin run at a much higher temperature than the rest. For example the extreme nose and the leading edges will reach 155° C. compared to the average 120° C. and these sections will be made of steel or titanium. Once more the matter of uneven expansion crops up for not only will there be different temperatures to contend with but the co-efficients of expansion of the different metals will not be the same.

The intending passenger need give no thought to all this but it does emphasise that flying supersonic is not just a matter of building the right shape of aeroplane, putting large enough engines into it and letting it fly. It will not be known for many years, if ever, just how much research that will help everyday life has gone into the supersonic airliner designs but it is quite certain that many people who never fly in their whole lives will obtain some benefit from the existence of these frequently-criticised aircraft.

Although the general statement has been made that normal aluminium alloys can be used for the Mach 2.2 type aircraft this does require slight amplification. The strongest light alloys are not entirely suitable because their creep-resistance is known to fall rapidly as temperature rises but aluminium copper alloys, which have been used extensively for engine components, are expected to offer the required characteristics. These alloys, which were originally available only as forgings, have been under test in sheet and plate form for some years and the results of many thousands of tests have been uniformly satisfactory.

Just as the Boeing company has been experimenting with various heat cycles to determine thermal fatigue in titanium, so has BAC been carrying on full life tests with the aluminium alloys. A complete airframe is currently (1965) being tested at the Royal Aircraft Establishment at Farnborough, including simulation of the various heat conditions which will occur in the full life of a Concord in airline service.

Much has been said about the effect of friction heating on the metals to be used in the airframes but it should be remembered that there are other materials involved as well. The transparencies such as windshields and windows have to be able to tolerate the same temperature variations and so do other non-metallic materials such as those used to house storm-warning radar scanners. Intensive research has gone into this problem and the information available shows that suitable materials are now available.

Recapitulating, therefore, the Concord design is claimed to have the following advantages. The so-called "gothic" wing planform provides a lift-to-drag ratio (L/D) of 8 to 1 in supersonic cruise and 14 to 1 in subsonic flight, the latter figure being of the same order as that for existing subsonic four-engined jets. A variable geometry wing, with its weight and mechanical complications is therefore not required and the fixed wing provides adequate fuel tankage space whereas the variable geometry aircraft would need a larger fuselage to accommodate the fuel.

The high angle of attack during the approach offers heavy drag as soon as the throttles are set for low power and this results in effective aerodynamic braking on touch-down. No additional air brakes need be provided, normal wheel braking and reverse thrust being all that is needed to bring the Concord to rest on a runway of typical length. It may be assumed that a braking parachute will be fitted for emergency use to all supersonic transports.

High rates of climb can be maintained right through the transonic range and it is therefore practicable to dispense with re-heat—and its attendant weight plus high fuel penalty—for acceleration to the supersonic condition, but it is planned to provide for re-heat if necessary.

The only systems which are new are the variable geometry air intakes to the engines and the fuel transfer arrangement to trim the centre of gravity to the moving centre of lift as the Concord goes through the transonic phase. Both these systems are easily fitted to other types of aircraft for extensive trials before the Concord makes its maiden flight.

The span of the delta wing is set at 78 feet and the overall length at 180 feet. These dimensions should give optimum handling conditions in flight but it is admitted that the pilots will have to get used to the peculiar effect of sitting perhaps 50 feet in front of the nose wheel when taxying. It is claimed that the wheel arrangement will permit the use of existing taxi-tracks on most airfields but turning a corner is going to give the pilots the impression that they are running off the track as the nose projects far over the grass. The position of the main wheels is expected to prevent the throwing of foreign matter into the engine intakes but provision exists to shield the intakes if full-scale tests prove this to be necessary.

Whatever may be the arguments for and against the two opposing designs it can be stated that the Concord is physically ahead of the American designs in that metal has already been cut at both the British and French factories, whereas the American designs have still not been approved (September 1965).

The original deadline for the selection of an American design from the projects offered by North American, Boeing and Lockheed was set back from 1 May 1964 to an undetermined date because none of the designs measured up to the demands of the F.A.A. Since then further design study contracts have been awarded to Boeing and Lockheed and it would appear that the North American design will not be taken any further.

The Lockheed delta is very similar in conception to the Concord and it is not therefore necessary to devote too much space to it. There are, however, certain fundamental differences. The Lockheed aircraft will be a Mach 3 design with a double delta configuration with the wing roots of the slim delta section carried almost up to the nose to take advantage of the leading edge vortices. Dissimilar in appearance to the Concord wing, it will use the same aerodynamic principles.

The "droop snoot" nose will be the only piece of variable geometry in the fuselage. The engines will be mounted separately, as in conventional subsonic jets, beneath the trailing edge of the wing. The aircraft is, of course, appreciably larger than the Concord and it is planned to carry up to 221 passengers. The wing span is at present set at 116 feet, the length overall at 222 feet 9 inches and the height to the top of the fin at 45 feet 9 inches.

Lockheed consider that a 15-year life may be anticipated, on the basis of 3,000 flying hours per year. This gives a life a little longer than that discussed by the other firms. It is also stated that the Lockheed aircraft would probably fly supersonic at an average height of 75,000 feet, somewhat higher than the Concord. The Lockheed contention is that sonic boom will be less offensive to those on the ground under these conditions but this problem is covered in another chapter.

All the designers are in agreement that the supersonic airliner, of whatever configuration, will be so aerodynamically efficient that its engine noise on and near the ground will cause less offence than is caused by the present series of subsonic jets. There is a mass of technical evidence to support this view but visitors to Farnborough and the Paris Air Show may require more convincing evidence than a lecture or a book can supply.

Simply because the British Aircraft Corporation and Bristol-Siddeley are the principal contractors for the British side of the Concord project it should not be assumed that the rest of the aircraft industry in the United Kingdom is sitting on the side-lines watching the chosen few do the work—and obtain the reward in cash and prestige. It is very unlikely that any firm in the industry has not had some part in the development of the new airliner but it will suffice to mention two very well-known names, Hawker Siddeley and Handley Page.

Hawker Siddeley is providing a great deal of the metal from which the airframe is being built and this alone represents quite big business. The aluminium alloys and the stainless steels that make up much of the Concord airframe are respectively quite expensive and very costly indeed. This may not seem to be a huge contribution but it has provided employment for a lot of people and is certainly vital to the construction of the airframe.

The Handley Page share of the work has been much more

publicised and a good deal more spectacular. This firm might be described as the rebel of the British aircraft industry because its founder, the late Sir Frederick Handley Page, refused to join in any of the plans for merging the industry into larger units. After his death the directors maintained his policy and there were many who predicted the collapse of one of the oldest firms in the business. However, there has always been a streak of obstinacy in the company and, although they have not participated in many of the production developments in high speed flight since they designed and produced the Victor V-bomber, their work has continued on a big and important scale in other fields.

When the design of the Concord was reaching something near finality it became necessary to carry on actual flight tests of the narrow-delta wing at low speeds to substantiate the theories that it would be manoeuvrable when near the stall in the landing phase of a flight. Handley Page was awarded a contract by the Ministry of Aviation to produce a flying test bed which was given the name of H.P. 115.

This aircraft, which had some similarity to a flying bomb of the Second World War, with its Bristol-Siddeley Viper jet of 2,000 lb. thrust mounted above the fuselage under the fin, had the greatest leading edge sweepback angle of any aircraft ever built, 75°. The H.P. 115 made its first flight from the airfield of the Royal Aircraft Establishment at Bedford on 17 August 1961 and it stayed up for 31 minutes.

The feasibility of the narrow-delta configuration with its vortex lift characteristic was fully proved during its years of flight at Bedford in the hands of test pilots of many nationalities but it was also found that all-round stability was higher than had been anticipated. From this work it was possible to say that the Concord wing would do all that was expected of it. The H.P. 115 has appeared at every Farnborough Air Display since that of 1961 and is probably the only forerunner of the super-sonic airliner to be seen in public—and by so many people.

This was not the only contribution to the Concord made by Handley Page. One of the major problems of any high speed aircraft is that of ensuring that the whole flight envelope is free from flutter. Handley Page pioneered a technique for this type of investigation which consists of using a low speed wind tunnel and a model. But the model is rather a special one.

The test model is made from a flexible foam plastic of carefully controlled density on a machined magnesium skeleton with the weight and stiffness distributions closely approximating to those of the actual aircraft structure. After static stiffness tests and weight checks, the model undergoes resonance tests to measure its various modes of vibration. Computer analysis of these test figures makes it possible to predict the flutter speeds.

Then the finalised model is mounted in a wind tunnel for tests of vibration at increasing wind speeds until the onset of flutter. The model, because of its flexible construction, is not destroyed and can be used again and again to give confirmation of the results. From these tests it is possible to confirm the validity of the theoretical predictions of flutter conditions and enable the designers to complete their work with certainty that the proto-type Concord will be flutter-free when it first flies.

At the other end of the speed scale is the BAC 221 slender-delta research aircraft. This aeroplane has a most interesting history, being, in its original form, the Fairey Delta 2 which first set the air speed record above 1,000 m.p.h.

This aircraft was taken over by the British Aircraft Corpora-tion and almost totally redesigned and rebuilt though it did retain the original Rolls-Royce R.A.28 turbo-jet engine and some of the major structural components. The Filton Division of BAC did the work on contract for the Ministry of Aviation and it, too, is being used by R.A.E. at Bedford for research into the aerodynamic and stability characteristics of the slender-delta wing, but, in this, case, primarily at the high-speed end of the range.

The wing shape is almost exactly that of the Concord and, although much general knowledge relating to supersonic flight is expected from the tests with the 221, it is clear that its work will be of great value in the development of the airliner. It is, in fact, the only aircraft in the world with the planform and performance range necessary to undertake the flight investigation of the aerodynamic concepts on which the Concord wing design is based.

The BAC 221 appeared at Farnborough in 1964, having made its maiden flight at Bristol on 1 May 1964 in the hands of the Filton Division's chief test pilot, Godfrey Auty. The research aircraft is not as fast as the Concord, having a maximum speed of about 1,060 m.p.h. (Mach 1.6) but there is claimed to be no substantial difference in the handling characteristics of this type of aircraft at this speed and at the planned Mach 2.2 of the Concord. The 221 has already done many flying hours.

13

CIVIL SUPERSONIC ECONOMICS

IN other chapters reference is made to the capital cost of supersonic airliners but there is inevitably a lot of guesswork involved in calculations of this sort. At the time when the Concord prototypes had advanced to the stage of cutting metal it seemed to be generally accepted that a purchase price per aircraft might easily be in the region of £5,000,000. The American design was still far from being finalised but estimates of up to double that sum were common. Whatever the actual figure may be there is no doubt at all that the purchase price is going to be not less than about three times that of the current range of big subsonic jets and all the airlines with routes suitable for SST operation have been, probably still are, wondering if they can afford to buy them. But can they afford not to buy them? This is really the $64,000 question and there seems to be no uncertainty as to the answer. They just must afford them or some other line, taking a financial chance, will steal all the traffic.

Experience with the subsonic jets was an unhappy one for most operators, but, oddly enough, not because these aircraft failed to live up to their promise. In fact they usually produced slightly better operating costs than had been anticipated and, in themselves, they have been a worth-while investment. It was the aircraft they displaced that put the airlines in the red. The last versions of the piston-engined airliners had to be disposed of, sometimes at little better than scrap prices, after as little as three years' service because the jets had arrived. Any line offering a service at 300 to 400 m.p.h. would very quickly lose out to a competitor offering the same journey in between one-half and two-thirds of the time. And the lack of vibration and noise of the big jet when compared to even the best of the piston-engined aircraft made them very competitive without the improvement in time schedules.

So the big jets were uneconomic because they forced their owners to take a heavy loss on earlier but otherwise good aeroplanes. And then came the threat that an even more expensive aircraft would be on the market—and would have to be bought for both prestige and practical reasons. It is not surprising that operators showed little enthusiasm for the SST.

As a general statement it is true that the subsonic jet operators acquired their full fleets by about 1960. There have naturally been many additions since then and more aircraft are on order while certain operators are even now only just moving into this type of operation. British United Airways is a good example, having only taken delivery of its first VC.10s in 1964, but, apart from expansion or replacement due to accidents, the delivery of subsonic long-haul airliners had passed its peak by 1960. Therefore, most of the subsonic jets had, by 1965, given five years' useful service and some even more than that. This compared favourably with the three-year period which was the life of many piston-engined airliners and when it became clear that no SST could possibly be in service before 1970, and probably later even than that, the prospect of re-equipping, though formidable, no longer looked impossible. If the jetliners which had cost around £2,000,000 apiece could have a minimum life of ten years, the amortisation rate annually would be £200,000 and even then there might be some return by selling to independent operators or by switching the aircraft over to freight purposes as was done with many of the piston-engined airliners.

On the basis of 3,000 hours annual utilisation, a perfectly reasonable figure, a long-range subsonic jet would make some 500 (more or less) Atlantic crossings in a year and, assuming that it carried only 70 passengers per trip (average) it would, in the course of ten years, fly 350,000 passengers on a route for which the fare averages about £100. Just £6 per passenger out of that fare does not seem unreasonable towards the cost of the aircraft. It works out at something like 0.0003 per cent of the total original cost of the airliner. A fair comparison with this cost to each passenger of about ½d. per mile would be the final writing off of a £750 car at the end of ten years with an average mileage of

25,000 annually. That would cost the owner ¼d. per mile. And he might consider himself lucky if a modern car stood up to a quarter of a million miles running.

Statistics of this sort are not very interesting reading but they are necessary if one is to understand, even vaguely, the problems facing the airline operator when he has to re-equip. On the face of it he will be able to consider purchasing the SST without accepting a heavy loss on his current investment. That undoubtedly makes his accountants a little more cheerful but then the question arises as to how long he can expect to keep his first generation SSTs in service before some enterprising manufacturer comes along with something even faster. And he is concerned with the running costs of the SST because it seems to be well established that, on the whole, passengers will not accept major increases in fares just because the flying time has been reduced. Increases due to changes in currency values have been absorbed by the passengers without too much grumbling but the halving—or thereabouts—of the flying time which came about when the big jets were introduced did not bring any real increase in fares in spite of the fact that all the airlines were more than financially embarrassed.

Taking the potential life of the SST first there does not seem to be any great risk that they will become outdated any more quickly than have the subsonic aircraft. Indeed, there is more than a fair chance that they will have to work for even more years before something better comes along. The reason for this is quite simple. No manufacturers could possibly afford to undertake the research and development programme needed to produce an aircraft with, say, Mach 5 or 6 performance unless governments provided the enormous sums of public money needed to pay for the work. And governments are already extremely unhappy about the huge costs involved in the development of the Concord and the American aircraft.

Even if this money could be found it is very questionable if there would be any great public appeal in an airliner which could cut the journey times of the SST in half. As things are the Concord should make the flight from London to New York in approximately two and a half hours, the American SST in fractionally less than two hours, start to stop. But the time taken on the ground is very unlikely to be greatly reduced between city centre and the airport and, with the best will in the world, Customs, Immigration and ticket formalities will probably not be greatly decreased from what they are in the mid 'sixties though more efficient methods may speed them up a little. Using the Concord the time from the centre of London or Paris to New York is likely to be in the region of six hours and a reduction of this to four and three-quarter hours will hardly make an overwhelming appeal to the passenger. It is true that doubling the speed on longer routes will have a more beneficial effect on the total journey time but the number of potential passengers is always less as the distance becomes greater, at least under the monetary systems which are in general use in the world.

So, though there is no question that ultimately there will be even faster airliners, there will be no great urgency to produce them and the estimates that the SSTs will give at least 45,000 hours utilisation suggest a probable life of 15 years—or more. £5,000,000 spread over 15 years means an amortisation rate of £333,333 per year and this compares reasonably with the rate for the subsonic jets. The possible figures are worth examination. A utilisation of 3,000 hours allows 1,200 Atlantic crossings in a year. Although the Concord will carry less passengers per flight than, say, a VC.10, the Atlantic traffic is growing steadily, increasing annually by perhaps 10 per cent on the previous year. It is not too optimistic to assume that the Concord might average 70 passengers per trip by the time it gets into full operation round about 1971. That would mean one aircraft would carry 84,000 passengers over the Atlantic in a year and a piece of simple division gives the answer that each passenger would have to contribute approximately £4 per trip to help to pay off the capital cost, a reduction of one-third on the current cost of subsonic jets. So, in that respect, at least, the SST is economically viable.

Airline operators will probably say that there are all sorts of other factors and many unknown quantities which make these figures into little more than guesswork. This may be true because it is almost impossible to estimate future traffic with exactitude but one has to start somewhere. Even allowing for unforeseen factors it is unlikely that the amortisation of capital cost of the SST will be any more of a headache than it has been for the subsonic jets. And it is a technical fact that the contemporary jets will have to be replaced after a life of round about 10 years. No aeroplane can remain in service, economically, when it is so aged that constant replacement of parts, sometimes major ones such as wings, is called for.

It seems fair to assume that the airlines could afford to buy SSTs—provided always that the world's air traffic could support the extra seating capacity that would be offered. The evidence seems to suggest that it will but the figures have been proved wrong during one recent period when the estimated increase in passenger traffic did not agree with what actually happened. And this occurred coincident with the huge capital outlay on big jets. Throughout the period from 1946 to 1964 passenger traffic in all countries of the world excepting Russia, China and a few satellites which are not members of the International Civil Aviation Organisation (I.C.A.O.) had risen annually by an average of 13 per cent. Suddenly, in 1957–58, it dropped to a mere 1 per cent, rose the next year to 13 per cent and then dropped again respectively to 8 per cent and 5 per cent, re-covering slightly in 1961–62 to 9 per cent and then, in the next two years rising to 12 per cent and 16 per cent.

In spite of the sudden lapse it is generally considered by the airline managements that an annual rise of 10 per cent is likely unless some international catastrophe such as a world war occurs. In 1964 no less than 156,000,000 paying passengers flew varying distances and on the Atlantic, which is an excellent yardstick for long haul operations of the busier kind, more than 2½ million passengers made the flight in one direction.

If the 10 per cent rise is maintained there should be 4,000,000 passengers on the Atlantic routes in 1970 when the first SST might be in service. At the same rate of rise there will be over

16,000,000 paying passengers using the Atlantic routes by 1985, the year in which the first generation of SSTs might be assumed to have completed their useful lives.

Reverting to 1970, however, it is possible to draw some conclusions about the situation from a revenue point of view though these will inevitably be very indefinite because the number of SSTs delivered in that year is most unlikely to be the total at present on order. Of those that are delivered—even if the early date of 1970 for service operation is achieved—not all will be on the Atlantic route.

The American SST is planned for up to 200 seats, the Concord for about 100. If 10 of each type are ready for service in the first year the total single journey seating capacity will be 3,000 and these aircraft could carry 4,000,000 passengers in a total of 1,333 flights, just about the number of flights that a 3,000-hour utilisation would permit.

When the operating costs are examined it will appear that the designers of the Concord anticipate that, even at the low revenue figure of 4 cents (U.S. currency) per statute seat-mile, a break-even figure of 70 per cent will be achieved. In other words, if these 20 supersonic airliners managed to get break-even bookings there would still be 1,200,000 passengers available to make use of those subsonic aircraft which were still in operation.

At the end of ten years' operation, i.e. in 1980, the traffic figure should have risen to 10,000,000 single journeys. On a break-even basis—with all the subsonic aircraft off the route except for purely cargo operation—there would be room for 60 SSTs, 30 of each type, on a 3,000-hour utilisation basis.

Clearly, if the operating costs can be kept down to an economic figure, the SST is a practical possibility on the Atlantic and on other long-haul routes and the numbers at present spoken for seem resonable in terms of the likely traffic build-up on the Atlantic and other routes which might usefully use the supersonic type of aircraft. At this moment in time, however, it does seem doubtful if the American estimate of a possible demand for 400 to 500 SSTs could be anywhere near the truth much before the end of the century.

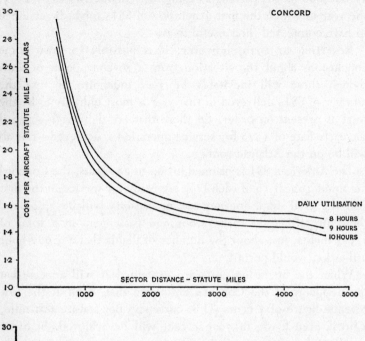

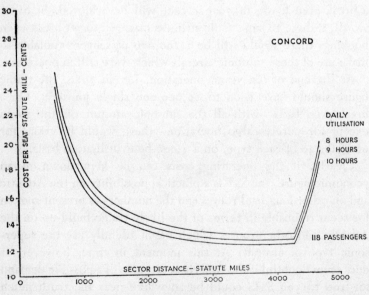

Concord cost curves

Above, maiden take-off of the TSR-2 from which so much was expected before the Government cancelled the order in 1965; *below*, Northrop F-5 Supersonic Fighter-Bombers

Left, the Gnat two-seater advanced trainer is now in service with the RAF. Powered by a Bristol-Siddeley Orpheus 100, the aircraft is super-sonic in a shallow dive over a wide height band; *below*, the US Air Force's T-38 Talon twin-jet trainer was the first supersonic aircraft to complete its flight testing pro-gramme without a major accident

For very obvious reasons the Americans have made no positive pronouncements about direct operating costs. Having no definite aircraft design approved it would be impossible to make any accurate forecasts but they have indicated that the alternative proposals would produce seat-mile costs comparable with those of the big subsonic jets.

The consortium of BAC/Sud Aviation has been rather more forthcoming and has published a forecast of seat-mile costs based on an all-economy class configuration, carrying 118 passengers on the Atlantic journey. It should be explained that the seat-mile cost is based on the direct operating cost, i.e. fuel, crew, maintenance, etc., plus an equal sum for administrative costs, insurance, passenger handling, training, agency fees, publicity, and the various extra items which go to make an airline tick. This basis has been found to be near enough to the truth for the accountants with other types of aircraft so it seems acceptable for the SST.

From the graphs published it is clear that on stage lengths of 1,500 miles or less the Concord is not competitive with the present generation of big subsonic jets and would be even less so with highly efficient medium-haul aircraft such as the Trident, BAC 111 and Douglas DC.9. But on the stage lengths for which it is intended, trans Atlantic for example, the cost per seat-mile is lower than that for the subsonic jets. For a utilisation of eight hours daily—approximately 3,000 hours per year—the direct operating cost is published as being fractionally above 1.3 U.S. cents per seat-mile on a journey of 3,500 miles. The cost per aircraft mile for the same utilisation and stage length is quoted as $1.44. (By unofficial international agreement these figures are usually given in American currency.) This would suggest an overall cost per seat-mile of 2.6 cents.

At the I.A.T.A. (International Air Transport Association) annual general meeting held at Bogota in September 1964, there was one estimate of the seat-mile costs of the Lockheed SST. This was given by J. F. McBrearty, Vice-President and SST General Manager of the Lockheed Aircraft Corporation. He suggested that the direct operating costs would be approximately 2 cents, with overall costs in the region of 4 cents, a materially higher figure than that for the Concord, and he admitted that his company's SST might be more costly on a seat-for-seat basis than the subsonic jets. Also at this meeting, E. C. Wells, one of the Vice-Presidents of the Boeing company, made an even less definite prediction but he did say that he thought the cost for long flights would be slightly better than with the subsonic jets. Perhaps his most interesting contribution on this subject was that his company considered that a daily utilisation of nine hours was practicable. That would put the yearly figure up to nearly 3,300 hours and, if maintained, would usefully reduce the capital cost per seat per journey.

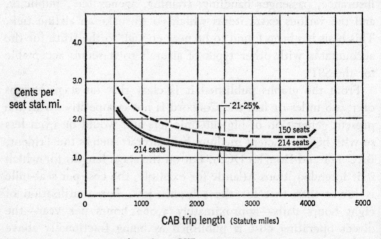

American SST cost curves

Mr. Wells did make one very significant remark which seemed to modify his rather optimistic views about the competitiveness of the SST with the long-haul subsonic jets which would be, he said, in the years ahead "refined". "Many advances would be required to provide a competitive SST."

Another factor brought out at this meeting was one which, normally, would seem to have little connection with the economics of supersonic flight, sonic boom. R. V. Carlton, of Braniff Airways—one of the firms which has placed orders for

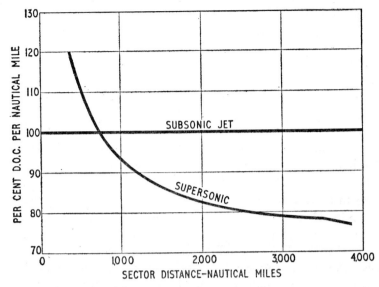

Subsonic/supersonic cost comparison

SSTs—said that it seemed that "to avoid intolerable economic penalties" the SST would have to operate round the clock with no airport or operational restrictions and no sonic boom restrictions in transition or in cruise. None of the representatives of the three manufacturing firms directly responsible for SST airframe design and production had any very convincing answer to this searching comment.

Looking back through this chapter the reader may well reach the conclusion that little has been learnt from several thousand words. That is the trouble with this aspect of SST operation, so much is guesswork. Inspired guesswork perhaps, but still incapable of final proof or disproof until the SSTs actually begin to fly. However, it does seem fairly certain that the long fatigue life of these aircraft and the unlikeliness of replacement by hypersonic transports before the end of the anticipated working life of the SSTs will allow the airlines enough time to amortise their astronomical investments in these aircraft.

14

CONCORD CONTROVERSY AND THE RUSSIAN
RIDDLE

WHEN the idea was first mooted that airliners could and should
be built for supersonic performance it was generally agreed that
there would be little point in designing an aircraft with anything
less than Mach 2 capability because only a really dramatic reduction in flying times could ever justify the enormous expense
involved in research, development and actual production. It is
true that Handley Page offered a basic design of an airliner to
fly at Mach 1.15 and seat 86 passengers but the advantage claimed
that it would produce no sonic boom, or very little, was more
than outweighed by the fact that the speed increase over the
VC.10 or the other big jets was too small to justify the cost.

The big operators were—perhaps still are—frightened at the
huge capital investment that SSTs would need and their fears
had some valid background. Students of aviation history will
recall that when the DC.8's and Boeing 707's were put on the
world's long-haul routes the operating companies found themselves with grossly inflated seating capacity in aircraft which had
cost around £2,000,000 each. For several years their annual
accounts had a predominance of red figures in them and deficits
assumed gigantic proportions. Extremely costly market research
had predicted a traffic growth rate which the facts did not
support and, for a time at least, the long-haul operators found
themselves in grave difficulties as the big jets sped across the
Atlantic with seating capacity for more than 120 people sparsely
occupied by a mere half-dozen at off-peak periods. It was very
natural that they viewed the arrival of even more costly-to-buy
and costly-to-operate airliners with grave misgivings.

However, to quote H. G. Wells in *The War in the Air*, "this
'ere progress, it keeps on," and the manufacturers, having

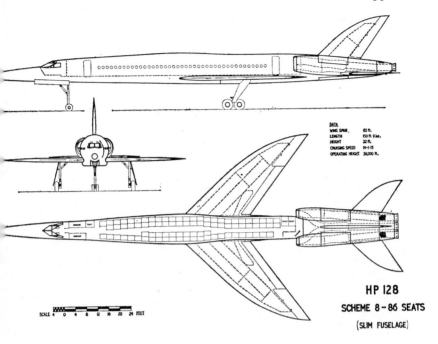

DATA
WING SPAN . 65 ft.
LENGTH 150 ft. 9 in.
HEIGHT 32 ft.
CRUISING SPEED M-1-15
OPERATING HEIGHT 36,000 ft.

HP 128
SCHEME 8 - 86 SEATS
(SLIM FUSELAGE)

SCALE 4   0   4   8   12   16   20   24 FEET

decided that Mach 2 airliners could be designed and built, quite
naturally wanted to build them. It was obvious that the fleets of
subsonic jets would continue flying for many years, as indeed
they will do, and that would make the order books of the aircraft
industry, with reduced military demand, more than uneconomic.
America had, of course, been considering the project but the
industry on that side of the Atlantic was in a far better position
than the firms in Britain and France. It was therefore reasonable
for the major manufacturers such as Douglas, Lockheed and
Boeing to bide their time. The European firms were virtually
faced with producing something new, something world-beating,
if they were to stay in business on their own account and not
just build American aircraft under license.

In the United Kingdom there were only two manufacturing
groups on a scale big enough to undertake so costly a design
study, and of these Hawker Siddeley was already committed to

extensive work on Vertical Take-off and Landing (VTOL) military aircraft. The field was reasonably clear for the British Aircraft Corporation to examine the possibilities while in France the Sud Aviation group, immensely satisfied with the success of the Caravelle, put much thought into the idea of a supersonic Super Caravelle.

In the meantime, the British Supersonic Transport Advisory Committee (STAC) under the chairmanship of M. B. Morgan and drawn from commercial and government establishments, was formed in 1956 to examine the project, then in abstract form. Three years later STAC reported in favour of a medium range aircraft flying at Mach 1.2 and a long range machine at Mach 1.8. A design study contract was awarded jointly to Hawker Siddeley Aviation Ltd. and Bristol Aircraft Company Ltd. (this was before the big mergers in the British aircraft industry took place). The purpose of this study was to evaluate the basic designs of an aircraft with a thick wing profile and integrated fuselage in the one case and a thin wing with discrete fuselage in the other.

In August 1961, it having been decided that the thin wing design was the better proposition, a further design study was completed which resulted in the Bristol 198, a light alloy, mid-wing, slender-delta monoplane powered by six Bristol Olympus jet engines mounted beneath the wing. A design for a Mach 3 aircraft to be built of steel and titanium was also submitted but this was dropped when estimates of time and cost for development had been fully considered.

It had been a requirement of the design study contract that co-operation with French, American and German aircraft manufacturers must be considered. The possibilities were examined but America held that a Mach 3 airliner based on experience gained with the XB-70 Valkyrie bomber would be the right answer and Germany was not interested—at that time—anyway. France, however, as stated earlier, was very interested and, like everyone else who had looked into the problem of financing the project, more than willing to consider any practical way of cutting costs.

At that time, 1959, Sud Aviation had evolved a design for a Mach 2.2 airliner, seating 70 passengers, having an all-up weight of 170,000 lb. and a range of only 2,000 miles. From this developed the much larger Sud Super Caravelle having full trans Atlantic range.

It was at this time, too, that the British Aircraft Corporation—which included Bristol Aircraft Ltd.—having decided that the 198 was too heavy—had produced a design for an aircraft designated Bristol 223, using four Olympus engines. When the British and French designers began seriously to compare notes it became clear that the two, independently designed, airliners, were immensely similar, perhaps an indication that the ultimate in efficient design had been achieved. The two companies had already worked well together on certain parts of the VC.10 which had been sub-contracted to Sud and now came the opportunity to cement this working partnership.

The two governments gave their approval and, in November 1962, a formal Anglo-French agreement was signed and the project was given the official name of *Concord*, spelt *Concorde* by France. So far as the engineers and designers were concerned the name could hardly have been more appropriate but unhappily this was not true at government level.

The cost of the design and prototype stages up to and including actual production tooling was originally estimated to be the staggering figure of £170,000,000—staggering that is to those who had not heard Sir Thomas Sopwith's estimate given to me some five years earlier. When asked if Hawker Aviation had any views about designing and producing a supersonic airliner he said he had no doubt at all that they could—provided someone was prepared to put up £200,000,000. He was not prepared to hazard a guess at what individual aircraft would cost the operators but he did go so far as to suggest that they might well be scared of such colossal investments.

Within a year or so of the signing of the agreement, fears began to be voiced that the original figure would be materially exceeded, a total of about £240,000,000 being the inspired guess. On the grounds that the original investment was so huge that it must be protected, the British Minister of Aviation in the Conservative government agreed that the work must go on. He did that publicly but there are no records available as to amount of wrangling and disapproval evident behind the scenes. The Socialist opposition in Parliament showed no such delicacy of feeling. They denounced this wanton waste of money and suggested that if and when they came into office there would be some new thinking. The fact that Britain and France were at least two years ahead of America, by this time working like beavers on design projects for a Mach 3 aircraft, and that an immense prize in money and prestige awaited the first to produce a satisfactory aircraft appeared to be of no interest to the Socialist party. Here was a magnificent opportunity to embarrass the government at a time when the country's economic position was, to put it mildly, suspect and the opportunity was not missed.

As the manufacturers had expected, the airlines had no choice but to examine the possibility of buying supersonic airliners if they were to become available. British Overseas Airways and Air France, after some delay, placed orders for eight Concords each but it will probably never be known how far national prestige and government pressures forced them into taking the initial step. Once they had committed themselves competing airlines had to follow suit or be left hopelessly behind. Pan American ordered six Concords and Trans World Airlines did the same. This was understandable as their routes overlapped those of the British and French operators but it was perhaps surprising that American Airlines and Continental Airlines, both primarily domestic operators in the United States, placed orders for four and three aircraft respectively.

Then Middle East Airlines, a very go-ahead operator based in the Lebanon, joined the queue with an order for two aircraft and the Australian line, QANTAS, whose chairman, Sir Hudson Fysh, had long ago said that Australia would be in the van when supersonic airliners came into service, ordered four. In all, 48 Concords were ordered in addition to the two prototypes to be built in Britain and France.

To say that these orders were absolutely firm and irrevocable would be stretching the truth. In fact the orders are hedged with conditions but a deposit of considerable size had to be handed over with each order and it would only be returnable if the Concord failed to meet the specification. If the orders were cancelled for any other reason the deposit would be lost and the customer would also have to pay a substantial penalty. Details of the deposits have not been disclosed but it is generally accepted that they total several million pounds.

In spite of the fact that the American SST design had still not been finalised by the end of 1964 no less than 93 of them had been "ordered" by the end of January 1965 and deposits totalling more than $9,000,000 lodged with the United States Treasury. The position created is a most peculiar one in a country intensely devoted to private enterprise. Because the Federal Aviation Authority had not accepted a design from any one of the competing firms, Boeing, Lockheed and North American, this government agency found itself in the position that it was selling non-existent aircraft and handling money for commercial concerns.

It might be assumed that the placing of orders for nearly 150 supersonic airliners indicated that airline managements were entirely convinced that they needed these additions to their fleets, even at a price up to £5,000,000 apiece. Nothing could be further from the truth. In fact, these lines have merely paid premiums on a new form of insurance policy, some of them placing orders for both types of aircraft so as to ensure delivery positions on the production line of whichever SST proved to be the best bet in the end.

The Boeing company has stated its belief that orders for the current range will eventually total about 450. Even by American standards this is big business. A turnover of around £2,000 million is a prize worth fighting for and this makes the conduct of the Socialist government elected in Britain in October 1964 very hard to understand.

When the new government took office one of the first official statements it made was to announce a thorough investigation of the Concord plans, accompanied by a very broad hint that Britain might back out of its agreement with France. The French papers carried suggestions that "perfidious Albion" was at its games again and the news even found its way on to the front pages of the South American papers.

A great deal of heat was expended and the flames were fanned when M. Pompidou, Prime Minister of France, said on 5 November 1964 that Britain might have abandoned the Concord project as a concession to America in return for the United States keeping quiet about the 15 per cent import duty surcharge which the new government had just imposed. M. Pompidou went on, "The position of the British Government is clearly to delay and in fact to abandon the Concord. We have not yet decided on our reaction."

These charges were made at a luncheon in Paris to the French Parliamentary reporters and naturally received wide coverage. In fact, the maladroit handling of a perfectly reasonable investigation by the new Minister of Aviation, Roy Jenkins, worsened considerably the already poor relations between Britain and Gaullist France.

In the House of Commons the following day the Minister made a statement in which he denied that Britain had decided to abandon the project but he left the position wide open and a stormy scene was only brought to a close when the Speaker adjourned the House. In his statement the Minister said that it now looked as if the overall cost of the project would amount to at least £280,000,000 up to the time the Concord was granted a Certificate of Airworthiness and might rise still further after that. He estimated that the purchase price of the aircraft would be £5,000,000.

The uncertainty remained for more than two months and the workers in the aircraft industry, of whom 25,000 or more were directly or indirectly concerned with the Concord, looked ahead to a very unsure future. It was not until 19 January 1965 that the British Ambassador in Paris, Sir Pearson Dixon, delivered a message from the British Prime Minister, Harold Wilson, to M. Pompidou to the effect that Britain would carry on with the Concord but even that assurance left the position about laying down a production line before the completion of the two prototypes as a very open question.

Some relief was felt in the industry but, in the meantime, another problem had arisen. The Mach 2 tactical aircraft, the TSR.2, also produced by the British Aircraft Corporation, had become suspect and it appeared that this, too, might be dropped. Some of the test flying in this aircraft would have been valuable to the designers of the Concord but the most important factor was that both types would use the Bristol Olympus engine and both development and production costs of the engines for the Concord would soar if the order for the TSR.2 engines—probably for around 400 of them—did not materialise. Once more the jobs of thousands of men in the industry or employed in the multiplicity of sub-contracting firms were placed in jeopardy.

There the matter rests at the time of writing except that the TSR.2 has since been scrapped, as mentioned elsewhere. The opposition tabled a vote of censure on the government for its methods in relation to the aircraft industry, a vote which was defeated by the government with a very tiny majority after a stormy debate in the House of Commons on 9 February 1965.

In addition to the battle between the European and the American manufacturers and the political skirmishes, there is also the factor of Russia to be considered. At the Paris Show, 1965, the Soviet Union showed a model of the Tupolev Tu.144, four-jet SST planned to fly in 1968. Very similar to the Concord and the Lockheed in appearance, the Tu.144 is expected to seat 121 passengers, fly at Mach 2·35 and have a 4,000 mile range. The gross weight is supposedly 286,000 lb. and it is hoped that it will be in service with the Russian airline, Aeroflot, in 1970-71. No dimensions or powerplant details were released.

The sketch here shows a forecast of another Russian SST based on the "Bounder" supersonic bomber but it is unlikely now that this will ever materialise.

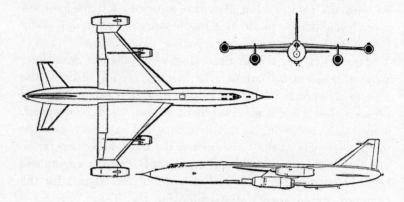

A possible Russian SST

Many authorities, including American, believe that the Russian aircraft will be the first of the SSTs to fly, perhaps the first to go into service but it is highly improbable that any will be sold to operators outside the Iron Curtain.

An aircraft in the Bounder category would probably be ideal for the internal airways of the Soviet Union where the major industrial cities are widely spaced, an average figure of 1,000 miles being representative. This stage length calls for less fuel and therefore a lighter-weight aircraft than is needed for the Atlantic or many intercontinental journeys and it follows that the capital cost can be lower.

Sonic boom problems will not be so acute with a smaller SST and, anyway, the government system of Russia, though far less despotic than that of Stalin, is not very likely to be unduly concerned by impassioned letters to *Pravda* or *Izvestia* complaining that the windows of the peasants of Yeneseisk had been blown out by the passage of Mr. Kosygin on his way to Yakutsk. This is not to suggest that no consideration to the problems of people on the ground will be given by the authorities of Aeroflot but in any regime where the State comes first, last, and in the middle, the feelings of the individual are not accorded the same importance as they are in the democracies.

There is no other estimate of when the Russians may go supersonic in their airline operations but guarded hints dropped periodically by the Soviet speakers, at home and abroad, imply that they may beat the West to it. Just as they put Sputnik I into orbit without any prior warning it may well happen that SST operation will be an accomplished fact before any announcement is made.

15

IS IT A HOSTILE ENVIRONMENT?

THE environment of supersonic flying is something quite different from anything the ordinary passenger and, indeed, the majority of aircrew, military and civil, have experienced. It also brings in other factors than the purely bodily ones such as air traffic control.

Taking the passenger aircraft first, since that is the type which will, in the final analysis, carry the greatest number of people at supersonic speed, there is a variety of hazards involved, hazards not met at the altitudes and speeds at which subsonic airliners normally fly, i.e. up to about 40,000 feet and 600+ m.p.h. First there is the matter of the cabin atmosphere. From a pressure point of view this must remain as at present with, desirably, a maximum cabin altitude of 6,000 feet. Some doctors who have specialised in aviation medicine consider that 5,000 feet would be better. With flights at as low as 60,000 feet this means that the external standard pressure will be 1.04 lb. per sq. in. against an internal pressure (6,000 feet) of 11.77 lb. per sq. in., a differential of more than 11 to 1. This is a staggering differential and one which makes the possibility of complete and sudden decompression—due perhaps to a window failure—one which cannot be entirely ruled out. Statistics show that partial decompression occurs about once in 20,000 flying hours in the lower altitudes of subsonic operation, i.e. once in every 12 million airline flying miles. It is clear, therefore, that complete decompression is at least a possibility from time to time under the greater pressure differential conditions. (A 6,000 feet cabin altitude at a cruise height of 40,000 feet, standard atmosphere, calls for a differential of 4.73, less than half that quoted for supersonic operation.)

Automatically operated oxygen masks are already fitted to the latest jet airliners for everyone on board but this is not really enough because body fluid boils at 63,000 feet and very serious physiological damage would result even during the short time it took the crew, presumably wearing pressure suits, to bring the aircraft down to, say, 10,000 feet. And this time would not be so very short because it would be unlikely that a descent at more than 5,000 feet a minute would be made so the operation would take ten minutes. And it is also stated by the aviation medicine experts that for ideal human reactions descents should not be faster than 500 feet per minute.

The safety factors needed in the construction of the pressurised parts of a supersonic airliner have, therefore, to be very high indeed if this danger is to be completely eliminated. Too gloomy a view should not be taken of the potential dangers but, once more, this problem shows why supersonic flight design is complex and very expensive.

At the operating heights the air is of low relative humidity and, even though it is compressed for use in the cabin, it remains exceptionally dry. The time at maximum height—and therefore minimum humidity—is likely not to exceed two hours with the present range of supersonic airliners but it is not pleasant and the consultant doctors have consequently recommended that a humidifying unit should be included in the pressurising system.

In the chapter on engines it has already been stated that the fuel will be used to cool the cabin air to an acceptable temperature but this air still has another invisible hazard within it at high altitudes. The ultra-violet light from the sun forms ozone in relatively large quantities above the troposphere (36,090 feet) the concentration reaching a maximum at around 100,000 feet. Even at the SST cruising heights the concentration is between six and ten parts in a million which is just 100 times as much as the human body can tolerate of this toxic gas for any appreciable time of exposure. Fortunately it is eliminated when the air is raised to a high temperature and this occurs in two ways. First the air entering the pressurising system is already at the skin temperature of the aircraft, about 150° C., and it is then heated still further by compression before being cooled in the fuel/air heat exchanger. Something like 90 per cent of the ozone is removed if the air is heated to 240° C. and the remainder, or almost all of it, can be removed by passing the air through a catalytic filter. So much for the hazards of the air, the "breath of life" which can become the breath of death if man fails to take precautions.

Cosmic radiation is the next danger to which the supersonic traveller is exposed. Once more, the belt of atmosphere round the earth gives protection up to heights far greater than even Mount Everest but the modern subsonic jets fly near the point at which this form of radiation could have some effect on the body.

Cosmic radiation consists of high energy particles reaching the vicinity of the earth from the sun and other sources of energy in outer space. The vast majority of these particles collide with existing particles in the atmosphere and produce mixed types of secondary radiation, all relatively or completely harmless even at current flying altitudes. However, above 60,000 feet there are increasing numbers of primary particles present and these can produce localised areas of damage in the body tissues. The earth's magnetic field deflects incident particles, especially those of low energy, and the dosage rate, at any given height, increases up to a magnetic latitude of about 55° N. (or south). In higher latitudes the rate stays fairly constant, the average at 75,000 feet being 2.8 millirem per hour. Precisely what the unit of a millirem is, is not really important to the layman but it provides a means of measuring radiation so that estimates may be made of the danger to persons exposed. The passenger may take heart because, even if he makes a number of flights over the Polar route in a supersonic airliner he is most unlikely to spend enough time at the required altitude to experience any danger.

Even aircrew will probably not be in any serious danger but if they should spend as much as 50 hours in a month at 75,000 feet in latitudes above 55° N. (Magnetic) they will be classified as "occupationally-exposed" in accordance with the recommendations of the International Committee on Radiological Protection. This means that they will have to undergo frequent medical checks and accept a maximum dosage rate which must not be exceeded. In fact, the danger is probably more imagined than real but it does exist and aircrew flying regularly at these altitudes and latitudes will be closely watched in the early stages of supersonic operation.

If that was the whole of the cosmic radiation problem there would be little to worry about, at least until still greater speeds and higher altitudes brought the radiation hazard so high that a single flight might give cause for alarm. Unfortunately there is another, very real, danger which will affect all high altitude operations and, again, especially those above $55°$ N. (At present the south latitudes are not really affected because there is so very little high altitude flying done there but that is a situation which will change so these remarks will ultimately affect the Antarctic just as much as the Arctic.)

Periodically what is known as a solar flare occurs and the frequency of this occurrence varies during an 11-year cycle up to a peak of 30 a month. When these flares happen there are high energy proton beams associated with them and the particle energy is very materially increased. Below 75,000 feet the effect is almost negligible but at that height events producing 15 millirem per hour occur about four times a year and, once or twice in four years events occur which produce 10 or more rem per hour, a rate nearly 1,000 times greater. This, of course, is highly dangerous and it is greatly hoped that methods of forecasting solar flares—and their intensity—will be discovered before SSTs start flying the Polar routes. Below those latitudes even these extreme events are not very significant but the doctors consider that provision must be made for re-routing all flights below $55°$ N. at danger periods and, if only 10–15 minutes warning can be given, aircraft must be prepared to descend and continue the flight below 50,000 feet. Radio communication is often difficult, sometimes impossible in high latitudes, especially at times of magnetic storms, so it is possible that warnings might not get through. This makes it desirable that a warning device should be developed for airborne use and almost mandatory that some form of dosimeter should be fitted to all SSTs.

That is about the limit of the hazards provided by Nature in the environment in which the SST will fly but there are other factors which affect the passengers, perhaps more than the crew. The lack of visual reference may create some odd sensations until passengers get accustomed to being, for all practical purposes, completely out of sight of the ground. It is true that many passengers sleep or read during a flight but if they do look out of the window during daylight there is usually something to see, however vague and indeterminate it may be. At 75,000 feet all detail on the ground—if it is visible through cloud—will be lost and there will be no sensation of movement at all.

Another thing which will seem strange, even slightly alarming at first, is the floor angle during climb and transonic acceleration. This will be much steeper than is usual with subsonic aircraft and it may seem that the SST is in a vertical climb. Steep descents will also be the rule and this may necessitate the use of seat-belts during normal deceleration and let-down whereas, at present, these are only put on during the later stages of the landing phase.

On the credit side, passengers may expect very little turbulence under cruise conditions because the narrow delta wings are not very sensitive to this condition of disturbed air. This is not to say that there is no turbulence at these altitudes because there is still a paucity of information on the subject but whatever there is will affect the airframe less than would be the case with straight or slightly-swept wing aircraft.

Some passengers have already had experience of the peculiar effects created by the change in local time when they travel in fast aircraft, especially if they have used the Polar routes. There, on a westbound journey it is possible to fly from Copenhagen to Alaska and, after several thousand miles, arrive—according to the local clocks—two hours before one left Scandinavia. In the reverse direction the day is severely truncated and this has odd effects, too. When the SSTs get into their stride this sort of thing will be common on all routes in generally east-west directions. It will literally be possible, landing in New York three hours before leaving London, to say "Tomorrow, when I took off from London . . .!" This may sound amusing but moving back on the clock or the calendar goes against all normal human experience and requires a degree of mental adjustment before it is accepted as routine.

The matter of Air Traffic Control does not directly affect the passenger because he is not concerned with directing the flight path of the aircraft. Indirectly it affects him very much. His personal safety is involved and so is his time. Consequently, the air traffic control authorities have to arrange that each aircraft flies along a path which does not coincide in place and time with any other aircraft and they have to fit the aircraft into a landing pattern which does not include any danger of collision or, normally, delay. There is nothing new in this situation but the problem is more complex with supersonic flight than with existing subsonic services.

It was stressed in an earlier paragraph that there must be provision for rapid descent from cruise altitude in certain emergency conditions and this implies that a captain will have no time to call the area control and obtain permission to descend as he does under the current rules. He will have to go down—fast—and be sure that his lane gives him complete vertical freedom. The only way he can be certain of this is by a change in the system which now gives vertical separation between aircraft on the same route and direction. Pilots demand a system of lateral separation as the only safe method and it may be added that they would welcome such an arrangement even now with the big jets flying at 40,000 feet. The need for rapid descent in an emergency is not so great as with supersonic aircraft but it exists.

Air Traffic Control argues that no navigation system is in being which can pinpoint an aircraft on the map with such accuracy that lateral separation can be safe whereas height can be determined within fine limits. So, though the authorities on the ground are sympathetic to the pilots, they do not feel that lateral separation is safe enough for normal operation, especially at the enormous velocities envisaged in the supersonic age. Here is deadlock which will, no doubt, be resolved but in the meantime it is probably the cause of the biggest headaches in the whole planning of supersonic commercial flying.

There is another factor involved in this business of vertical freedom. Airliners not only provide a service, they are also supposed to make money. There are cynics who point out that they never do but the principle applies even if the results leave something to be desired. Once the SST has reached cruising speed it is more economical in fuel to let the aircraft gradually drift up as fuel is burnt and the airliner becomes lighter than it is to climb in a series of steps. Step-climbing can be done by arrangement with Air Traffic Control, stage by stage, but cruise-climb is continuous and therefore demands complete vertical freedom from the initial supersonic height up to the maximum the aircraft will reach. Again the authorities are sympathetic but they hold that the question of making or losing money is not their affair, they are concerned with air safety first and foremost. However, the increased fuel requirements for step-climbing are materially important and this type of flight costs appreciably more money. Presumably this may affect the fares charged so the passenger is now directly interested in the problems of Air Traffic Control.

All jets are inefficient at low altitude and burn fuel at a higher rate and this will be even more noticeable with the SST. As a result the operators would like to have priority in landing but Air Traffic Control is unwilling to give this privilege. And they may not be entirely unreasonable in holding that all aircraft deserve the same treatment—except in emergency. Some sort of average pattern will develop when these aircraft come into service but it is inevitable that some time will have to be allocated to hold-off before landing and this, too, is going to cost the passenger money.

Still on this question of cost, flight time is important or another reason. The capital cost of the SST is going to be very high compared to earlier aircraft and each passenger will have to pay some portion of it based, not on the miles he flies between point A and point B, but on the time he spends in it. Any delays will have to be paid for and the cost per minute may be anything from three to six times as much as for a subsonic aircraft. Once more the passenger is interested in air traffic control methods.

From the foregoing it might seem that no passenger will ever show up to buy a ticket. This is most certainly not going to be true and support of that positive statement lies in the fact that every advance in airliner speed has been followed by increased traffic. If one looks back to 1931 when the Schneider Trophy was won outright at little more than 300 m.p.h. there can hardly have been anyone who seriously imagined that, in less than 20 years it would be normal for passengers to fly at the same speed and, ten years later, at twice the speed. But it must be acknowledged that the SST brings with it a lot of new problems and potential hazards which have to be overcome to the satisfaction of the more critical would-be passenger.

We are perhaps more frightened by the radiation business than by any other single risk which high altitude flying includes and it may well be that the public relations departments of the airlines will have to produce some clever propaganda to offset the critical comment which will inevitably arise, especially among those who are half-informed.

16

AIRLINE PILOTS HAVE THEIR SAY

IT has been an oft-repeated complaint that the pilots who have to fly the military or civil aircraft are never consulted about the design until the aeroplane is in production and it is too late to make anything but minor changes. The complaint is not wholly fair because the test pilots are consulted and their views will at least go some way to coincide with those of the men who fly the machines in regular service. Nevertheless, it is illogical to ignore the men with immense experience when a costly project is still in a malleable state.

The experience that airline pilots had when they were handed the present generation of subsonic jets and told to fly them made a deep impression, particularly on the senior captains, and, through their professional associations, they made it clear that this must not happen again. Most countries have an Airline Pilots' Association and these bodies are all members of The International Federation of Airline Pilots' Associations. This organisation asked the British Airline Pilots' Association to mount a meeting in London at which the manufacturers could state their cases and members could ask questions, give their opinions and generally try to make these opinions felt in time for the voice of experience to have some effect on design and operation problems with supersonic airliners.

A Symposium was held at the Piccadilly Hotel, London, from 12 to 14 November 1963 inclusive. Present were pilots, many of them senior captains, from twenty-two airlines and nineteen Air Line Pilots' Associations. In addition there were representatives from numerous government departments, covering research, meteorology, air traffic control and, of course, the Royal Air Force plus technical men from every one of the airframe, engine, instrument and operating equipment manufacturing firms. In all, nearly 500 men and a few women were in the hall when the Duke of Edinburgh, himself a pilot of wide experience, opened the meeting with some very trenchant remarks.

The tone of the occasion is best represented by quoting—at some length—from an agreed policy published by I.F.A.L.P.A. to coincide with the symposium. As might be expected, the views expressed were forthright and left no doubt that these men would not countenance the introduction of any SST which did not measure up to the highest operational and safety standards. For instance, the introduction to the statement of policy read:

"Any attempt to introduce supersonic aircraft on a commercial basis before their problems have been resolved to the satisfaction of I.F.A.L.P.A. should be resisted by the Federation and its pilots. SST aircraft should commence operations in airline service only after the necessary meteorological, navigation, communications and ATC systems and services are proved capable of effective day by day use (up to all flight levels within the aircraft's capabilities) and the equipment has been installed and satisfactorily tested under operational conditions for the routes being flown."

"NOTE. The reference to 'Systems and Services' is intended to apply to the personnel operating those services as well as to the actual items of equipment."

This leaves no doubt that the pilots are determined that the big change from subsonic to supersonic is not going to be foisted on them until they are ready. Another quote shows strikingly the attitude of pilots to those whose lives they have to guard.

"SST civil aircraft should be regarded as unacceptable to the pilot unless they are so designed that, under all foreseeable emergencies, the chances of survival of the passengers and the cabin attendants must be either the same as, or the equivalent to, those intended for the operating crew members."

And, a bitter memory of the restrictions which some pilots regard as actually dangerous in the operation of subsonic jets:

"The SST must not prove itself such a nuisance that the pilot in command is prevented from operating the aircraft according to the optimum procedure."

Various other requirements by the pilots prove conclusively that this time they will not be prepared to accept any sort of make-shift solutions to navigation or air traffic control problems. In the work programme section of the policy statement they say:

"The Federation believes that the ATC system for the SST should be supra-national in character, be positive, place no reliance on the 'see and be seen' rule and be supported by a navigation system sufficiently reliable to permit safe operation at the envisaged separation standards."

Some fifteen quarto pages of type make up the complete policy statement and little is left in the way of loopholes through which designer, operator, airport commandant or air traffic control officer could crawl if he had any idea of imposing unacceptable conditions on the SST pilots. It is perhaps a pity that this document cannot easily be made available to all airline passengers and inhabitants of houses within audible range of major airports. If it could be these people might not feel that airline pilots were quite such aloof and remote beings as sometimes appears. If a similar opportunity had been given—or been made—before the introduction of the subsonic jets there might not be the crop of complaints from those who lose sleep and from pilots who feel the restrictions endanger their flying and the people down below.

The meeting was broken down into panels, at each of which several speakers presented papers dealing with special aspects of the SST project. Then the delegates were given the chance of joining in the discussion after each paper had been presented. Panel One dealt with general design; Panel Two covered Flying Characteristics and Controls; Panel Three was devoted to Operational Problems; Panel Four handled Flight Planning and Operations; and Panel Five, the last formal section, included a wide range of Environmental Problems. The Symposium terminated with a closing address by the Rt. Hon. Julian Amery, Minister of Aviation, but this speech was preceded by a description of a hypothetical SST flight from London to New York, with command of the flight shared, section by section, by five senior airline pilots of varying nationality.

The aspects of supersonic flying dealt with in Panels One and

Two have largely been covered in earlier chapters of this book but the Operational Problems which formed the subject of Panel Three are of interest.

The Assistant Director of the American Aviation Weather Services read a paper on the meteorological angles of SST operation. He went into some detail about what the weather men could tell the SST crews, what he thought would be their most vital demands in the matter of forecasting and what still had to be learnt so as to meet these demands. He summarised his talk as follows:

"1.   Take-off. No greatly differing problems from those of to-day's subsonic jets.

2.   Acceleration and Climb. Selecting altitude and area where environmental conditions will be the best for optimum engine performance and especially related to the temperature conditions.

3.   En-route. Need for more precise and advanced information on the condition of the flight environment. This would include information on winds, temperatures, precipitation, and other pertinent meteorological parameters in the layer, 40,000 to 80,000 feet.

4.   Deceleration and descent. Accurate information concerning areas of possible icing and convective cloud formations.

5.   Approach-to-land and landing. Most critical problems of the entire operation: determining and forecasting wind shear below 1,500 feet, and more accurate methods of measuring, reporting and forecasting visibility values and cloud height information.

"To solve these problems and others, *many of which we may presently be unaware* (Author's italics) will require the concerted effort and co-operation of those interested in the success of this great forward step in air transportation."

This last candid admission by one of the leading meteorological authorities of the world gives conclusive proof of how valuable was the idea of this pilots' get-together. This was just the sort of lack of knowledge which they wanted to get ventilated so that when the SSTs go into service the problems will have been anticipated and solved before unexplained accidents happen.

In the same Panel the whole problem of noise and sonic boom was discussed but this is the subject of another chapter and the comments will be handled there.

Dr. G. Bennett, of British Overseas Airways, presented a paper on "Some Human Factors and Limitations". He started by dealing with pressurisation problems to be considered with Mach 2.2–3 aircraft operating at between 60,000 and 75,000 feet. He pointed out that, even though a very high standard of reliability has been achieved in the current range of subsonic jets, partial decompression results from some malfunction once in every 20,000 flying hours. This is not normally a serious matter at the operating heights involved and the provision of automatically released oxygen masks makes the eventuality into little more than an inconvenience.

However, at 63,000 feet the body fluid boils. In the event of complete decompression it would be absolutely necessary that one or more crew members should be wearing pressure suits in addition to oxygen masks. Presumably the passengers would just have to put up with it while the crew dived the SST to more acceptable altitudes but clearly this is a factor which could make the more imaginative type of passenger think several times before venturing into an SST. He did suggest one solution, an emergency supply of compressed air which would cover the period of the emergency descent procedure.

In Chapter 15 the matters of ozone and radiation were mentioned. Dr. Bennett also dealt with these before going on to consider acceleration and deceleration. In this respect it appeared that it might be necessary to use seat belts during the transition from supersonic to subsonic flight for those in forward-facing seats. On the other hand, the steep angle of climb after take-off—perhaps 20°—would probably preclude the use of rearward-facing seats, however desirable they might seem to be for other reasons.

The doctor also drew attention to the psychological effects on both passengers and crew of the peculiar time changes which would affect them when flying easterly or westerly routes.

Hazards and emergencies completed the work of Panel Four. Panel Five was devoted to environmental problems, air traffic control, navigation and instrumentation, communications and, as with all the other panels, wound up with a discussion in which pilots were able to ask some extremely pointed questions on the problems which still remained to be cleared up. Then came perhaps the most instructive period of all, a hypothetical SST flight, conducted by five captains, each taking a specific phase of the flight and handling it in accordance with the conclusions reached during the various Panels. With permission from the International Federation of Airline Pilots' Associations, this is reproduced in full in Appendix A together with the report of the discussion which followed.

The Symposium closed with a speech from the then Minister of Aviation, the Rt. Hon. Julian Amery. Like most politician's speeches it was remarkable for a complete lack of information about government intention but it left the impression that the Ministry would welcome the opinions of the men who would, one day, fly the SST, and far more surprising, that the Ministry might even pay some attention to those opinions.

This question of the men who will fly these aircraft is naturally one which is engaging the interest of the airline managements. Presumably the captains who at present fly the subsonic jets will be among the first to command SSTs but there has to be a second generation ready to take over and the intake from Air Forces is steadily declining as missiles tend to replace manned aircraft. The problem of pilot recruitment is therefore a very real one, even for the slower, short-haul aircraft, but the added problem of selection of those who, in the ordinary course of things would expect to command a Concord or similar type in due course is not an easy one. Some idea of the long-term view taken by some airlines can be gained from the fact that Aer Lingus, which recruits ten or more Irish boys of $17\frac{1}{2}$ years of age every year for training as pilots, is already taking into account that they may ultimately be responsible for an aircraft costing £14 to £15 million. Personnel selection which has to look so far ahead is indeed a tricky business.

THE MEN WHO WILL FLY THE SST

EVERY new phase of flying has produced its crop of apparently devil-may-care pilots and some of the more spectacular accidents have fostered the idea in the public mind that any man who flies a fast aeroplane has no consideration for his own neck or that of anyone else. It may be that some of the record-breakers of the inter-war period were a little careless of their own safety but, having known quite a few of them, I think it would be true to say that when a crash landing was inevitable they did everything possible to avoid hurting other people, in or out of the aeroplane, and to protect their property.

Lindbergh, for example, was known as the "Flying Fool" because he attempted to make a solo Atlantic crossing in a single-engined aircraft in 1927. It is true enough that most people would not regard this flight as the sort of thing that would appeal to a life insurance company but the fact remains that the risk he took was a calculated one. Anyone who has read his book, *Spirit of St. Louis,* will know the deep consideration that was given to every item in the aeroplane, the care that was taken in selecting an engine and in checking the history of failures during long running periods on the test bed. Only a few years later Lindbergh became technical adviser to one of the world's biggest airlines and this certainly does not suggest any inherent foolishness. But his flight was one of the most spectacular ever made, and the world's press played up the danger angles to the limit on the perfectly sound basis that their readers would not be remotely interested in his meticulous hourly checks of fuel consumption, but they would revel in an account of how he spun down and only recovered level flight as his wheels skimmed the water.

This type of example could be repeated ad nauseam but it

suffices to mention just one other group of dashing, brave, heroic, use any other superlative that comes to mind, band of fighter pilots who routed the Luftwaffe during the Battle of Britain and probably won the war by doing so. One attacking twelve; one squadron defeating a force of fifty or more fighter-escorted bombers; this was terrific stuff to watch or read about and it was certainly dangerous as the casualty lists proved. But it was not foolhardy recklessness; if it had been, Germany would have come out on top in 1940. It was the result of intensive, well-directed training and the most careful study by individual pilots of the enemy tactics.

Many of the demonstrations given by fighter squadrons at air displays look extraordinarily dangerous and, carried out by less skilled pilots, they would be. In fact they are no more dangerous than other forms of military flying and the rarity of announcements in the press of an R.A.F. crash is proof that military flying—in peacetime—is not dangerous.

It is an education to fly with one of the crack squadrons and see for oneself the meticulous care that is given to the pre-flight checking, the consideration for the passenger's comfort during a flight in which he might be subjected to unpleasant physiological strains such as high G stresses, the official caution that sonic boom is directed away from land, and from ships wherever possible.

Certainly the men who first "broke the sound barrier" as the newspapers loved to call it, took risks that could not be wholly calculated. Neville Duke, in his account of the early test flights in the Hunter, tells how, at somewhere around Mach 0.95, vibration started in the tail and the rudder kicked. Then the control column moved forward and all his strength would not avail to bring it back again until he had managed to lose speed.

The late John Derry, in an address to students of the Royal Aeronautical Society, made a significant remark. "Contrary to public opinion, the test pilot must possess a good fear!... A complete absence of fright will result in poor tests and often in catastrophe." Nothing devil-may-care about this attitude.

The pilots who first fly the supersonic airliners will not be chosen from the youngest group of available airmen, they will be men of, probably, young middle age, with immense experience behind them in command of subsonic airliners. They will possibly appear to be very remote characters, even more so than the present generation of airline captains because their flight time will be so short on a three to four thousand mile journey that they will barely get an opportunity to meet their passengers. This fact may create the impression in the minds of the passengers that these men, this élite corps, are somewhat aloof but they will actually be no different from other airline captains, merely men with more to achieve in less time.

On the face of it the impression might be created that a flight of this kind involved less work and strain for the captain and his co-pilots than is the case with slower aircraft. So much of the flying will be done by automatic means, almost by computer programme, that the crew will have little to do except watch the machines do the job. In a sense this is true but the watchfulness demanded will be even greater than it is in subsonic aircraft.

It is highly improbable that the autopilot system will go wrong during supersonic cruise. Far too many precautions and duplications are introduced to prevent any failure materially affecting the progress of the flight but mechanical or electrical failure is not completely impossible and the pilot in charge has to be prepared to meet the challenge if it should arise. At a speed of 25 miles per minute any sudden deviation from course would have dire effects on everything not strapped down and the passengers will presumably not wear their seat belts during this sector of the flight. Sudden decompression of the cabin—again a most unlikely but not utterly impossible occurrence—would call for even quicker action by the pilot, presumably already wearing his pressure suit, to get the aircraft and its human load down below the level at which their body fluid would be boiling. This type of mentality does not and cannot go with a casual approach to the day's work and the pilots chosen for supersonic services will have to be men of mature judgment, not easily rattled, and they will have to give an appearance of

THE MEN WHO WILL FLY THE SST 159

competency as well as be competent. Though there will be some enthusiasts among the early travellers in the SST, a great many passengers will go aboard with certain doubts, certain reservations, especially if they know that the outside of the cabin will be much above the boiling point of water during most of the flight!

These pilots—the captains in particular—will have another problem to face. This problem already exists but it will be infinitely more pronounced when they move from subsonic to supersonic operation. In addition to their duty to the passengers and themselves, the duty of arriving in one piece and as nearly on time as possible, they have to fly the aeroplane economically for the benefit of their employers. As was pointed out in an earlier chapter this duty sometimes requires a double loyalty, the one to the employer to arrive on time with as much unburnt fuel in the tanks as possible, and the other to Air Traffic Control to fly the aircraft in such a manner as to reduce the ever-present collision risk to an absolute minimum. The two things might seem to be one but, unfortunately, shareholders and boards of directors sometimes expect their captains to take short cuts— provided they are not themselves passengers at the time. To reconcile demands which may pull in diametrically opposite directions calls for qualities of determination that even the best technical people do not always have.

This is especially true in civil aviation where Air Traffic Control is almost inevitably run by the government of the country and is therefore cautious, sometimes to a farcical degree. The captain knows perfectly well that some of the modifications to his flight plan are quite unnecessary and will cost huge sums in the fuel account, sums which his airline accountants will bitterly resent spending. He will be expected to use his personality to persuade the controllers to accept his plan without modifications but he will not be expected to arouse bad feeling by doing so. In other words, in addition to being a technician of high standing, a social success with any passengers he may find time to meet, a man of quick and reliable judgment and exceptionally good physical health, he also has to be an ambassador who could wheedle concessions out of a country which had just handed over an ultimatum that would result in war.

By this time the reader may have come to the conclusion that he will never have to fly supersonic because there will not be any crew capable of handling the aircraft. Happily, this is not so. Pilots seem to be a breed which can produce these apparent prodigies in fairly large numbers. Already, some of the airlines which are recruiting second officer material are selecting men, boys rather, who have it in them to take this enormous responsibility and not lie down under it when their turn comes in 15 or 20 years to command, perhaps, not a supersonic but a hypersonic aircraft.

But let no one envy the captains of the first SSTs. Theirs will be a wearing responsibility with air traffic controllers still new to the job, however much simulator time they may have put in, passengers looking for new thrills yet afraid they may get them in greater quantity than they are prepared for, the world's press, radio and television watching every move, and the directors of the line looking anxiously for any slip that might damage the future possibilities of a new venture, a venture that has cost untold millions of hard-earned—or hard-borrowed—money.

Yet when those of us who are privileged to be on board do make that first flight to New York from London, we shall be greeted by a smiling captain who will leave the impression that it is all just another piece of cake. What he will think, privately, of us, when we leave the aircraft is quite another matter but it is greatly to be hoped that we, at least, will go away with some understanding that he, and his crew, if not supermen and women, are something far above average and that they are really earning the several thousand pounds a year, perhaps six thousand, which is being paid into their banks. This applies to captains, of course. First and second officers are certainly not going to be in that bracket, neither will the stewardesses.

The test pilots who have flown—and in some cases still do fly—the supersonic aircraft make an interesting study, too.

They are not so young as many people think. A cross-section of the British ones makes this very clear. Naturally, there are many others employed by the manufacturers and by the R.A.F. and Ministry of Aviation but the ones selected are mostly well-known and very senior in their profession.

Godfrey Auty, who quite recently took up the BAC 221 on its maiden flight, is chief test pilot of BAC Filton Division, and he is 44. (All the ages given are based on the planned date of publication of this book.) His flying life goes back to the R.A.F. in 1940.

Roland Beamont, currently deputy chief test pilot of BAC is 45 and he started flying in the R.A.F. in 1938. This gives him some 27 years of flying and he was actively concerned with the latest marks of the Lightning and the TSR.2.

Bill Bedford, as he is affectionately known throughout the aviation world, is the same age and he started flying with the R.A.F. in 1940. As chief test pilot of Hawker Siddeley he has been flying supersonic aircraft for more than a decade and still does.

G. Robb Bryce, chief test pilot of BAC, is a year younger than the last two, but he became chief test pilot of Vickers Armstrong (Aircraft) in 1951 and has been closely concerned with very fast aircraft ever since. His flying started in 1939 with the R.A.F.

Ronald E. Clear, an experimental test pilot with de Havilland, was born in 1917, started flying training in 1933, became a test pilot in 1940 and at the age of 44 was still actively flying all types of aircraft at Hatfield. He is perhaps not so well known to the Farnborough public as some of the others but that does not make the work any less demanding.

John Cunningham, chief test pilot of the de Havilland side of Hawker Siddeley, was also born in 1917. His serious flying began with the Auxiliary Air Force in 1935 and he has been concerned with high speed aircraft ever since. At the age of 48 he is one of the most active of the test pilots in Britain.

Neville Duke, who was chief test pilot of Hawker Aircraft until he met with a bad accident, was born in 1922 and joined the R.A.F. for flying duties in 1940. He stopped test flying in

11—SF

1956 at a younger age than most of the others but this was purely due to his accident. It did not stop him flying, however, but he went on to less exacting work.

George Hazelden, chief test pilot of Handley Page since 1947, was born in 1915 and started flying in 1939. He was not directly concerned with supersonic flying but it is generally accepted that the Victor has exceeded Mach 1 in the dive and it is a very fast aeroplane. Hazelden is 50 this year and has announced his intention to retire to a more peaceful job.

Jeffrey Quill, of Vickers Armstrong, is not so much in the limelight to-day but he was one of the first to be seen regularly flying very fast aeroplanes at Farnborough. Born in 1913, he began flying in the R.A.F. in 1931 and was still active up to and beyond the period of the Swift, becoming head of the military aircraft section of Vickers in the late 'fifties.

Brian Trubshaw is another of the very active test pilots. Born in 1924, he was appointed chief test pilot of Vickers Armstrong in 1960, some 18 years after he started flying in the R.A.F. His work has been very much associated with extremely fast aircraft.

In other countries a similar state of affairs exists. The test pilots are men of mature judgment and a large number of those who take on the really great responsibility of trying out totally new aircraft or new theories are men past their first youth and often in their forties.

18

SONIC BOOM A MENACE?

NOISE has become a very serious problem indeed in aviation, particularly civil aviation, in view of the proximity of major airports to large cities and built-up areas. That some of the complaints made by people on the ground are quite frivolous does not alter the fact that great annoyance, actual distress and even damage to property close to international airfields are factors which cannot be swept aside and forgotten. It is not surprising, therefore, that fears that the position will further deteriorate when supersonic transports are in use have been voiced by large numbers of potential sufferers.

It is too early to make positive predictions about take-off noise levels of SSTs but there is some reason to believe that they will not exceed those of contemporary subsonic jets in spite of the fact that the total thrust available will be between 50 and 100 per cent higher than that of present day aircraft. It is not anticipated that full power will be needed for take-off and, additionally, developments in noise reduction techniques have already done something to make more tolerable an admitted nuisance. If these optimistic forecasts are borne out in practice there is hope that the situation will get no worse than it is now. If it is any consolation to those who have been deafened by re-heat take-offs at the Farnborough Air Display it can be stated categorically that the noise level at London Airport when a Concord leaves the ground will not be so bad as when a Vulcan or Victor goes up under maximum thrust.

Those living within a few miles of an airport may, however, be more fortunate than they are at present. The steeper climb of the supersonic airliner will allow the aircraft to reach a greater height more quickly and, with a basic noise level of the same order as for subsonic jets the annoyance should affect a smaller total area. It has been stated categorically that over-shoot noise levels will be no greater than those currently permitted for night operation over urban areas.

So, though those presently troubled by straightforward engine noise may gain little advantage, it is reasonable to state that they will suffer no additional disadvantage. Others, now immune from aircraft noise by virtue of the height at which they operate, may be faced with a new hazard, sonic boom.

This phenomenon has been the subject of a great deal of uninformed hysteria and a picture has been built up of citizens living on international air routes being subjected to a fusillade, day and night, of the magnificent bangs that were such a feature of the big international air displays some years ago. "Breaking the sound barrier" seemed to be a literal fact when showmen like Neville Duke, Bill Bedford and the late John Derry aimed their aircraft at the crowds at Farnborough and dived through Mach 1. The earth did tremble, quite a lot of material damage was done and this gave rise to the idea that an overpowering thunder-clap would accompany every supersonic airliner throughout its flight and leave a trail of damage comparable to that caused by Hurricane Flora or one of its equally devastating sisters.

In simple terms a sonic boom is a strong pressure wave through the air created by an aircraft moving at or above the speed of sound. The intensity of the boom is affected by the size of the aircraft and the height at which it is flying. The pressure wave occurs at the nose and the tail of the aircraft and these waves spread like ripples in a pond, creating cones of pressure—to use the term which has come into general use—which travel along with the aeroplane. The illustration will show how the pressure wave takes up the form of a cone and trails behind the aircraft. It must trail behind because the SST is travelling faster than sound while the pressure wave travels at sonic speed.

It is clear from this simple picture that—above a certain point—the higher the aircraft is flying the narrower the band in which the pressure wave is felt on the ground. The intensity of the wave—or boom—is also affected by the height but the speed and physical size of the SST are also factors of importance.

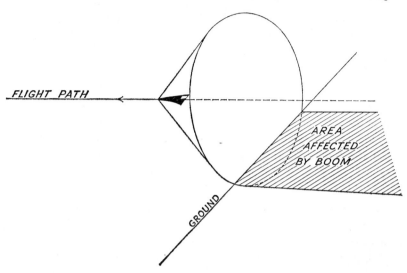

Although it is generally thought that sonic boom begins when the aircraft reaches the speed of sound this is now accepted to be not quite true. In fact the boom apparently begins at a speed of about Mach 1.13 and, of course, ceases when deceleration brings the speed back to that Mach number. Even this is not quite the whole story. If the aircraft is climbing it is possible that the pressure wave will—for all practical purposes—never reach the ground due to normal refraction processes. Mr. M. G. Wilde, of the British Aircraft Corporation, read a paper at the airline pilots' Symposium on the subject and showed that this effect was normally negligible except in the region of Mach 1.13. At higher velocities the climb angle required to prevent the wave reaching the ground quickly became impossibly high, for example, at Mach 2.0 the climb angle required would be 30.1°.

From all this it does seem that if supersonic transports are going to operate over land the people below will have to learn to live with sonic boom but they will only do this if the over-pressure is kept down to acceptable levels. What these levels are must clearly depend on individuals but some figures are available which give a guide. Tests have shown that an over-pressure of 0.5 lb. per sq. in. above current atmospheric pressure is barely noticeable, even to the most sensitive, and at three times that overpressure only isolated complaints are received. When the overpressure rises to 2.0 lb. per sq. in., however, especially if the occurrences are frequent, it becomes, as Sir George Edwards described it, "an unjustifiable nuisance". It is thought that the Concord when flown at its normal 50,000 to 60,000 feet will produce a boom acceptable to the public but the larger Mach 3 transports planned by America will need to fly 10,000 feet higher to bring the boom down to the same level.

The whole business is still somewhat of a mystery because no aircraft comparable in size with the planned SSTs has ever flown at speeds above Mach 1 and there is no clear evidence. Nevertheless, before supersonic flight over land in Britain was stopped there were some authentic claims of damage to property in the Farnborough area and compensation was paid by the Air Ministry when investigation proved that the claim was a genuine one. A false picture quickly built up as soon as it was known that a benevolent government department was handing out money and a very large number of opportunists who had acquired broken windows or cracked ceilings waited until an aircraft produced a bang and then put in a claim. A similar state of affairs existed in America so a most comprehensive series of tests were started with Oklahoma City as the "guinea-pig" in the spring of 1964 with a view to sorting out the wheat from the chaff, and, incidentally, getting a mass opinion poll on what the ordinary citizen would tolerate.

The tests went on for six months with U.S. Air Force F-104 fighter aircraft making supersonic flights several times a day over the city at heights between 30,000 and 40,000 feet. Each flight produced sonic boom and the noise was heard by 700,000 people. The Federal Aviation Authority set up a complaint centre and fitted eleven houses with measuring equipment operated by trained crews. In all, 1,277 passes were made over the city and about 13,000 letters and phone calls were received at the complaint centre. These included 3,248

claims for damage but after a thorough—and sympathetic—
examination 186 of them were accepted as valid and a total of
$4,500 compensation was paid, mostly for broken glass and
cracked plaster. And, it was said by the F.A.A., most of these
cases of damage were apparently caused by a few flights in which
the pilots produced higher overpressures than the—so-called—
acceptable level for airliners.

It cannot be assumed that this test is the final answer, indeed,
the U.S. authorities admit that it isn't. The F.A.A. Deputy
Administrator for Supersonic Development, Gordon Bain, told
the U.S. National Aeronautic Association, that tests would have
to continue—round the clock—and large aircraft such as the
XB-70 would be tried. This optimistically assumed that the one
and only prototype of the XB-70 would reach speeds of Mach 2
to Mach 3.

Mr. Najeeb Halaby, Administrator of F.A.A., told a press
conference that the United States would not cut metal to build
a supersonic transport until the sonic boom problem had been
solved. This announcement, which must have given great pleasure
to the inhabitants of Oklahoma City, might have been more
convincing if the United States had then had an acceptable design
for such an aircraft. Perhaps that is unduly cynical and it must
be admitted that the U.S.A. is showing genuine interest in a
real problem.

Britain has conducted no official tests over urban areas but
it is alleged that unofficial flights have been made over certain
parts of Wales. A crop of claims that cows had aborted and
hens had stopped laying eggs seems to have followed every bang
and Ministry officials have been hard at work trying to sort out
the genuine from the false. This is reminiscent of the early
railways when every farmer within earshot of a new line bom-
barded the companies with frivolous claims for damage and it is
a pity that it should be so. The authorities, contrary to the views
of some extremists, do not want to cause trouble and a variety
of false claims makes their task infinitely more difficult than it
has to be.

The position is perhaps not quite so desperate as some would make it out to be. The initial supersonic route will unquestionably be over the Atlantic and it is relatively simple to plan flights so that the transonic and supersonic phases take place entirely over water, thus eliminating annoyance to people down below. At the same time it will be simple to conduct exhaustive tests of sonic boom effects on the surface by stationing ships along the routes—the weather ships are already in position—and taking all the necessary measurements. By the time supersonic routes are extended to land areas it may be assumed that the sonic boom will no longer be a cause of damage, annoyance or even minor irritation.

No chapter on this subject would be complete without reference to Bo Lundberg, Director-General of the Swedish Aeronautical Research Institute. This man has conducted a campaign for several years against the SST on a variety of technicalities but his main reason for opposition is sonic boom.

According to Bo Lundberg the problem is an insoluble one but some of his pronouncements are based on assumptions that do not seem to be entirely sound. However that may be, his comments make interesting reading and, even if there are some who disagree with him, it must be admitted that his efforts are directed always to the creation of a more silent world and for that he should be praised. But the earnest enquirer is advised to question the sources of his statements; the evidence does not always seem to support them.

19

THE ANCILLARIES

TO go into the details of all the ancillary equipment needed in a modern aircraft would require a book of several volumes on that subject alone. It is estimated that about one-third of the cost of a modern military strike aircraft is devoted to the supply and installation of the electronics alone. This is a subject so rigidly tied up in security that it is quite impossible even to give an outline but the airliner, though not involved with weapons systems, will have to include a certain amount of the same types of equipment for navigation, etc. Here security is not quite so difficult and a little can be said on the subject.

The sheer speed of the Concord—and even more the American SST—makes it necessary that navigation shall be nearly perfect. The most minute deviation from course will take the aircraft many miles off its planned track and the cost in fuel in returning to the correct course will be no small item. This situation is made worse by the fact that changes of course during supersonic cruise will have to be made very gently indeed or the passengers will suffer from the accelerations caused by the turn. There is virtually no alternative to the use of an autopilot system controlled by a computer, programmed before the flight starts and amended by the inclusion of any new facts which may come to light during the flight.

It is true that wind speed variations from the forecast speeds and directions will not have so much effect on the SST as they do on subsonic aircraft but an unexpected jet stream of 150 knots at right angles to the line of flight can have quite marked effect on the position of the aircraft. And in case the reader thinks this an unlikely condition to arise I would just say that such a jet stream did affect a Royal Air Force aircraft in which I was flying near the North Pole only a year or two ago. I was present at the met. briefing and it was not forecast though the existence of jet streams in those latitudes is always recognised as being possible without prior warning.

By feeding a suitable output from the Doppler equipment into the flight computer it is possible to make instantaneous corrections of course if such eventualities arise and keep the aircraft much more accurately on track than could be done by any other means.

This is not, of course, the starting point for the in-flight navigation system but it shows very clearly how necessary some sort of flight director or computer is for supersonic operation. The old methods of navigation which were barely adequate at 400 m.p.h. are relatively useless at Mach 2.2 or Mach 3. In the former case the aircraft is travelling at 25 miles per minute, in the latter 33 miles per minute. Celestial navigation, while it would certainly give easy readings on sun, moon or stars, would be so extraordinarily slow that it would be useless. By the time the navigator had worked out the calculations based on his sights he would be several hundred miles away from the point at which he started. The same principle applies with the use of Loran or some modification of the wartime Gee. The period required to get the position on the map would be appreciably less than with the celestial method but it would still be slow and cumbrous, giving very out-of-date results.

The only solution is some form of flight log which shows, on a moving map, the position of the aircraft throughout the flight. Even here there are some difficulties. Both Gee and Decca are relatively short range aids unsuited to operation over large stretches of ocean. There is the long-range Dectra system which can operate over the ocean and this has possibilities for the SST when it starts on the Atlantic or Pacific routes. And it is very accurate indeed.

Even with this instantaneous method of presenting the positional facts to the pilot there is still the problem of putting in the necessary corrections and this takes too much time if handled manually. The errors therefore have to be converted into control signals of one kind or another so that the autopilot is continually corrected so as to maintain the planned course and height.

The Sperry inertial navigation system can do this with the aid of its latest floated gyros with hydrodynamic gas spin bearings and a digital computer using microminiaturised circuitry. Latitude and longitude plus course and cross-track error are all presented visually to the pilot but they can also be fed as corrections to the autopilot and to the main computer to enable it to work out a new flight programme to meet the changed conditions if, for example, a new set of wind conditions occurs.

Elliott Automation Ltd. is closely involved in this matter but before going on to detail the exact part this company will play in the equipment of the Concord here is a quote from an address by R. W. Howard of that group to a meeting of airline pilots. He had been discussing certain aspects of automatic flight and navigation control and he went on:

"Perhaps the most readily seen example . . . is in the navigation system. Our own work on supersonic military aircraft navigation systems, which appears to be supported by B.58 (Hustler) experience, is that some form of automatic derivator of aircraft position, and perhaps steering information, is necessary at speeds in the region of 20 miles per minute. A digital computer could provide continuously, or on demand, aircraft position both in latitude and longitude, and also relative to check or reporting points, together with E.T.A., course to steer, etc. Moreover, if fuel flow and fuel contents information is supplied too, it can provide continuous 'how-goes-it' information, range remaining, diversion range remaining, etc. Since the computer will have a stored knowledge of the aircraft's performance characteristics currently contained in cruise control and flight manuals, it can indicate to the crew on demand optimum flight conditions for the particular ambient atmosphere at the time.

"All of this type of information gathering and processing and system performance monitoring is currently done by the crew and the proposed use of the computer is merely a means of removing the chores of frequent sums and reference to charts and tables which might otherwise be necessary.

"BUT PLEASE NOTE that all the systems and information remain directly accessible to the crew so they can ignore any computer if they wish and calculate their data in their present manner. Thus computer failure has only the potential effect of increasing their workload and does not incapacitate any basic systems."

This very concise commentary on the value of automatic flight control methods may be encouraging to those who like to think that the captain and his co-pilots are the final arbiters in the technical problems of flight but the fact still remains that they would not have the time to do "all the chores of frequent sums, etc." in the course of a flight from London to New York. Therefore the weight—which is not very serious—and the complexity—which is—of all this electronic navigation equipment is something the operator has got to face. Elliott Automation, in concert with the French firm, Société Francaise d'Equipements pour la Navigation Aérienne, and the Bendix Corporation of America, is developing the automatic flight control system for the Concord and this will include automatic landing, the electrical trim system, the auto-stabilisation and the auto-throttle systems. All the firms concerned have had wide experience in the design and construction of electronic equipment for supersonic as well as subsonic aircraft.

Weather radar is another vitally important item of equipment for the SST. In supersonic cruise it is reasonable to suppose that the aircraft will be above the weather, though there is not much information about clear air turbulence at the heights likely to be used. But at the height and place chosen for the acceleration from subsonic to supersonic flight it will be absolutely necessary for the crew to have an accurate picture of the weather conditions. Acceleration through a thunderstorm, though not necessarily dangerous, would certainly not be the free choice of crew —or passengers—and the forecasters will often not be able to give precise locations of these storms at certain times of the year.

Communication equipment will certainly have to be more complete than in subsonic aircraft. Signals initiated by the crew will continue to be by voice as they are now—at all stages of the flight—and communications prior to landing will be much as at present. Other signals coming in such as weather reports and routine traffic from the ground are expected to come through an airborne teleprinter to save valuable crew time in reading and writing down long messages.

Flight data recording apparatus will probably be carried in greater quantity than hitherto because it will be essential to keep accurate records of a very large number of parameters of flight in the new type aircraft. Skin temperatures alone will create a demand for many more recording channels than are needed in subsonic aircraft.

Mention was made in an earlier chapter of the problems of cabin pressurisation. This equipment already adds an appreciable amount to the dead weight of a passenger aircraft; in the SST it will add even more. The heat exchangers to spill the heat of the intake air into the fuel cannot possibly be light and may add very seriously to the non-paying load of the Concord and other types. Cabin wall insulation, whatever means is chosen, though taking up no more space than in subsonic aircraft, will inevitably be more costly. And whereas, in contemporary airliners, the need for pressurising and temperature-controlling the baggage and freight holds has not been one of paramount importance; in the SST it will be. Even a bottle of after-shave lotion might do queer things if the suitcase it was stored in was raised to a temperature of 120° C. And in the American aircraft with a skin temperature reaching up to 300° C. there could be really dangerous accidents in the baggage or freight compartments.

The electrical demand in a modern airliner is very large indeed. It will be even bigger in the SST with its greater variety of control systems all using electricity in one form or another.

On the credit side is the fact that the length of each flight will be very short indeed and the galley facilities should be correspondingly reduced. But to offset that will be the inclusion of more comprehensive humidifying equipment to keep the cabin atmosphere in a reasonable state and that may add weight equivalent to the amount saved in the galley and the food and drink carried.

As it takes longer to descend—even at an emergency rate—from 70,000 feet to an acceptable altitude than it does from 40,000 feet if the pressurising fails, the supplies of oxygen will have to be materially increased. Compressed or liquid oxygen does not, of itself, introduce a very large weight penalty but the containers are extremely heavy.

These are only a few of the special ancillary services needed in the SST but enough has been said to explain why such an immense number of companies engaged in so many different trades are concerned with the design of the SST and why such extensive—and intensive—research and development is going on. The cost of the airframe alone is going to be frighteningly high but it would be interesting to know just what all the other items are costing to develop to the required standard. This figure never will be known *in toto* but it must be a staggering one.

It is now normal practice for the routine ground checking which has to be done after each flight to be completed with the aid of an electronic exploring system. This saves many man-hours and is probably more efficient because it is constructed so that it cannot miss a test in its built-in check-sheet without notifying the operator that it is not "working to rule". Now the complexity of the SST is so great that work is going on to develop an airborne version of the same instrument. Programmed by a computer, the test rack runs through all the pre-engine-start checks and only when it has a "good" answer for every one of them is it possible for the engines to be started. A similar device is being prepared to carry through all the pre-take-off checks and, again, all the pre-landing checks. This matter is a serious one but one cannot help wondering what the machine does if the pre-landing checks are unsatisfactory. It is easy to understand that it could prevent engine-start or even take-off but the imagination is severely tested in respect of a landing check failure. Does the SST have to go on flying until it runs out of fuel?

Seriously, though, there is much to be said for this project. A number of crashes have occurred because some item in the check list was overlooked and anything which will dispose of this quite unnecessary hazard in flying is worth money and a weight penalty.

The instrumentation of the production aircraft, though simplified as far as possible to reduce the number of instruments the pilots have to watch, is going to be in massive array. This is nothing to what the prototype aircraft will have to take up on the test flights. When the first instrumented VC.10 was on its flight trials it carried 15 TONS of instrumentation. It seems likely the first Concord will carry a comparable amount.

All the normal instruments available to the pilots are repeated on racks in the cabin plus a number which are not of immediate flight interest. These are arranged so that they are photographed almost as fast as a ciné camera would work. And for safety this apparatus may be installed in duplicate because it is cheaper to do that than to pay for the fuel for one flight which aborted because a camera mechanism had jammed.

Then there are the strain gauges which provide electrical signals which have to be recorded, usually on magnetic tape. These may be in hundreds but they could equally well be in thousands when an entirely new type of wing is being used. Coupled with these gauges are transducers which produce signals relating to every movement on the control surfaces and these must be recorded against the same time scale as the strain-gauge signals which show how the wings react to the various evolutions of flight.

Even that is not the entire story of this phase of recording. Complex electro-electronic-hydraulic systems are involved in the movement of the control surfaces and these are initiated by signals from the auto-pilot or the auto-throttles or, alternatively, by the actions of the pilot using the manual controls. Every one of these stimuli has to be recorded so that computer analysis can be made of any normal or abnormal set of circumstances that test pilots and designers may wish to examine in detail.

Crash recorders which can be ejected from the aircraft in the event of an accident or which are so strong and so fireproof that they can survive the worst crash ever conceived are also carried, these instruments recording all the essential parameters which should explain what went wrong. (This type of instrument proved itself when the BAC 111 crashed fairly recently, killing all the crew. Within hours the cause of the accident was known.)

It is normal to include records of barometric pressure and temperature, outside the aircraft, but the SST will provide yet another vital series of readings which will have to be taken during test flying, the temperatures resulting from air friction. It will be necessary to take these at a variety of points on and in the airframe and probably a more complete than usual analysis of engine temperatures will be needed.

During all flights, test or otherwise, there will certainly be full recordings of the quantity of cosmic radiation falling on the outside of the airframe and the quantity penetrating it. There is still a certain amount of man-made nuclear radiation floating about in the upper atmosphere in the form of radioactive particles and the degree of exposure to this hazard will have to be measured and recorded at all times. Ozone percentage in the cabin air is another parameter not previously regarded very seriously but it will be in the SST.

The scientists will, no doubt, think up other measurements they would like to take, certainly checks will have to be made of the electronic side of the flight direction, navigation and computing when long trips begin, but what has already been listed here can easily make nonsense of a mere 15 tons of test instrumentation.

After each flight all the records have to be examined and this entails a battery of computers and an army of programmers and analysts. And, just to make sure, it is now becoming common practice to telemeter all the essential parameters of a particular experiment back to the ground by radio where designers and other test pilots can observe what is going on almost as well as the airborne crew. This is particularly valuable if a test which could be dangerous is being carried out. With modern techniques it is now possible to fit closed circuit television systems into the aircraft so that items normally invisible to the crew can be observed in flight or, in the case of the undercarriage, during a landing. These pictures can now be recorded and they

Right, Squadron Leader Neville Duke, former Chief Test Pilot of Hawker Aviation; *below*, *left*, Group Captain John Cunningham, Chief Test Pilot of de Havilland; *below*, *right*, the late John Derry, Test Pilot at de Havilland

Left, Godfrey Auty, Test Pilot in charge of trials with BAC 221; *below*, *left*, Georgi Mosolov, the Russian pilot who set the speed record at more than 1,650 mph in 1962; *below*, *right*, Roland Beamont, the Test Pilot responsible for the Lightnings and TSR2

CHOP THRO CANOPY
FOR EMGCY RESCUE

can be transmitted live to the observers on the ground so that, once again, if anything untoward should happen the explanation should not be hard to find.

It is considered likely that a television system may be incorporated in the production aircraft to allow the crew to watch the undercarriage during taxying operations. The cockpit may be as much as 100 feet ahead of the main wheels and this can cause some unusual effects when negotiating corners on the taxi-tracks.

During 1964 Hawker Siddeley evolved a technique in connection with test of the Autoland equipment in the Trident which will almost certainly be followed when flight testing begins with the SST. The tape records taken of all the parameters relating to approach and landing—I.L.S. signals, autopilot responses, control surface reactions, undercarriage performance, etc.—were fed, via a computer, into the ground control rig set up for experimental work in a hangar. By this means the whole of a landing sequence could be repeated on the ground, in slow motion, or even on a start-stop basis, to allow physical examination of every mechanical operation which took place in the air.

Although there may be practical difficulties there is no theoretical reason why the heat simulation system to which the complete SSTs will be subjected on the ground should not be controlled in the same way from actual recordings made in flight. And, since money is being spent like water on these projects, it could be arranged that all the airframe stresses are reproduced on the test airframe while the correct heat cycle is being applied. With some uncertainties still about fatigue life under the varying heat conditions this would be an immensely valuable piece of investigation, both for the SST and for a variety of other applications of aluminium—or other—alloys under mechanical as well as heat stress.

Flight simulators are now almost as much a part of a new aeroplane as is the aeroplane itself. At the time of writing no simulator has been ordered for the Concord and, since the final design of the American aircraft has not been approved there has clearly been no opportunity to design a simulator for pilot training. Nevertheless, Trans World Airlines, the first operator to place an order for the American SST, has already sent flight crews, widely experienced in the subsonic jets, to operate an SST simulator—designed on the general plan for such an airliner—at the Langley Research Station, Hampton, Virginia, of the National Aeronautics and Space Administration. The purpose is to let crews with extensive knowledge of the problems, practice fitting the SST into the existing traffic patterns into and out of Kennedy International Airport (formerly Idlewild, New York).

By this means it is expected that it will be possible to study the characteristics of the SST in the air traffic control pattern and determine the effects of the A.T.C. system on the SST design requirements and operating techniques, making it possible to consider design modifications—or changes of procedures—which would allow the new aircraft to be integrated into the traffic pattern without the headaches that accompanied the arrival of the subsonic jets on the world's air routes some years ago.

It is likely that when the SST simulators arrive they will be able to include the recording/replay technique described earlier, making even more realistic the behaviour of an aircraft while the training crew is still on the ground. Much of the work in a simulator with contemporary aircraft is, of a necessity, a matter of making the crew *do* things. In the SST their job will be more one of checking that automatic devices do the things correctly. In this context, the repetition of actual flight conditions could be an extraordinarily valuable training medium, particularly if the unexpected had happened during a test flight. And, while there is certainly no wish to stress the matter of accidents, they do happen in aviation and the use of the flight-data record in a simulator to repeat the conditions preceding the accident would perhaps be even more of an object lesson than a printed-out computer analysis could ever be.

This chapter has been very largely devoted to the electronics, either airborne in the SST or associated with it in some way on the ground and it may seem that undue stress has been placed on this aspect of the new airliners. That is how it is. More and more the aircraft is directly or indirectly controlled by electronics, radio, radar, computers, television and straight process control. Existing airliners would be lost if all the electronics could be removed, the SST would simply never exist at all.

One subject has not been mentioned at all; mainly because nothing has been published on the matter. But it is vitally important and its provisions will cost quite a lot in weight as well as a material sum in money. That is fire prevention and control. Existing aircraft are well equipped and, in spite of some of the horrific stories which appear from time to time in the papers, it is very seldom indeed that a modern aircraft takes fire while airborne. They frequently burn after hitting the ground but it is most unusual for a conflagration to start before that. However, with the SST the problem is surely going to be a lot more complex.

The fuel, once supersonic cruise is achieved, is going to be very hot indeed and, although Dr. Hooker went into this matter with the fuel companies and decided that all would be well, this is only because of the special precautions which are being taken. If a can of paraffin was placed on a gas cooker and taken up to more than 150° C. there would be no question as to what happened. It would explode and scatter blazing paraffin all over the place. Remove the precautions and the Concord would do the same thing when flying at Mach 2.2.

It is already known that the tanks will be inhibited by filling the system with nitrogen or some other inert gas but the possibility of leakage can present a very serious hazard. Design—and manufacture—to prevent leakage is one of the really important fire precautions and the installation of a very complicated fire detection system is another. Added to this will be, probably, a network of foam or carbon dioxide piping to allow smothering of any tank which might light up in addition to the normal engine safety measures. Certainly, if such a network is not used, some alternative protection will be needed to deal with spontaneous ignition if something does go wrong with the inhibiting system and oxygen finds it way freely into a tank at a dangerous temperature.

Most of this chapter has been devoted to the SST because it is of far wider general interest than military aircraft. But, harking back to the electronic equipment, military aeroplanes are even more heavily loaded with such gear than civil airliners. Low flying attacks demand contour-following radar tied to the auto-pilot, no small item in itself. Then there is the target locating equipment, air-to-air, which not only has to find out the precise position of the target but also, through a computer, exactly where it will be when the missile, which may cost almost as much as the carrier aircraft, arrives at—it is hoped—the right place and time to destroy the raider.

Reconnaissance aircraft, too, carry an immense weight of gear in excess of that used even as recently as 1939–45. A battery of cameras, vertical and oblique, is now standard equipment but beyond that there is television gear which enables the recce pilot to send his pictures back to base with nearly as much detail as he can see himself. Even the ordinary cameras are far more complex than the ones familiar to World War II veterans, in that they can get from adequate to perfect pictures at low level while flying at speeds up to 1,000 m.p.h.

Armament is clearly a matter of choice for the mission involved and has little to do, directly, with the fact that an aircraft is supersonic. Flight re-fuelling equipment is needed in some military aeroplanes and, though this process is not carried on at supersonic speeds, it does introduce additional complications. For example, the probe at the extreme nose of the aircraft will reach very high temperatures in supersonic dash but it must not be distorted, even fractionally, if successful re-fuelling is to be carried through without waste of time—or fuel.

When the Labour Government issued its ultimatum that the British aircraft industry would get less orders there was an outcry that the electronics industry would be dangerously affected. Perhaps this chapter explains the justice of that outcry a little more clearly.

20

THE MORE DISTANT FUTURE

MUCH of this book is devoted to the future of supersonic flight so it may seem superfluous to look still further ahead. However, most of what has been said so far only relates to the future in the sense that the work is not completed. Basically, the plans for Mach 2 and 3 aircraft are very much in being and metal has already been cut for the Mach 2 civil transport.

The real future lies in still further increases of speed with resultant effects on methods of propulsion. Most long term projects tend to be obsolescent before they are actually complete pieces of hardware and it looks as if the supersonic airliner is in the same class as battleships, aircraft carriers and new cars in this respect. It is significant that no less an authority than Dr. B. N. (Barnes) Wallis has stated that he considers nothing less than Mach 5—approximately 3,000 m.p.h.—can be an economic proposition. Dr. Wallis has so often been right since he first started designing airships before the First World War up to the present day that it would be most unwise, and certainly discourteous, to reject his opinion out of hand. He put an immense amount of time and thought into the design of a variable geometry aircraft for Mach 5 and it can safely be assumed that financial considerations were not overlooked in his research.

What is surprising is that, as early as September 1962 the Minister of Aviation stated that the Royal Aircraft Establishment was already studying the problems of manned sub-orbital flight at Mach 14, more than 9,000 m.p.h. This was advanced thinking indeed but it was not based on the tortured dreams of some over-worked boffin. Rolls-Royce designers had put forward a scheme for driving an aircraft at speeds up to Mach 15—just on 10,000 m.p.h.—using a combination of pure jets—or ram jets—or turbo rockets—to accelerate the airframe well into the supersonic speed range and then change over to an *external* combustion "engine" to take the speed up to its maximum.

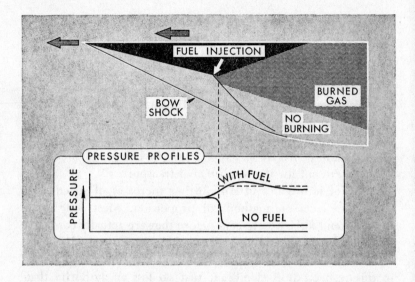

It has been found that shock waves seriously upset the flow of air through the engine when high Mach numbers are reached and the efficiency of any form of jet engine falls off above Mach 4.5. But it is possible to achieve thrust exceeding drag if fuel is burnt on a specially designed surface at the rear of the aircraft without shock wave troubles intervening. This fact was discovered by research teams working at John S. Hopkins University and McGill University, under the direction of Dr. D. L. Dugger, and Rolls-Royce was encouraged to produce a basic design for an aircraft which would take off under the power of four turbo-rockets and climb to about 100,000 feet reaching Mach 5. At this height the external ram jet would take over, the rockets would be shut down, the configuration of the underside of the airframe would change to that shown in the accompanying sketches, and the aircraft would continue to accelerate until it was cruising at Mach 15 at 200,000 feet.

This is all very interesting and, if Rolls-Royce, a conservative organisation, goes as far as to publish the project in some detail,

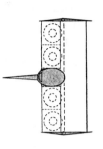

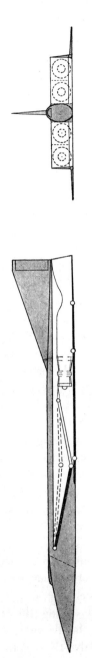

LOW MACH NUMBER CONFIGURATION

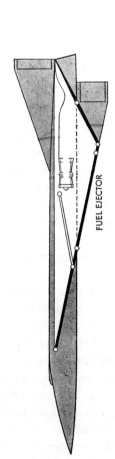

FUEL EJECTOR

HIGH MACH NUMBER CONFIGURATION

probably a practical development might be flying before 1990. From a military point of view it may be assumed that the faster troops can be carried to a trouble spot the better the chance of maintaining peace; but is it any use for civil transportation?

The earth is a very small place when speeds of this magnitude are being considered. The greatest distance from any point to any other is 12,500 miles, about 1¼ hours flying at Mach 15. On the face of it this is fine, only a half day excursion is needed for any journey—and return—in the world. Unfortunately, it's not as simple as that. The Mach 15 aircraft has to accelerate to its cruising speed and decelerate prior to descent and landing, and there lies the problem.

It was shown at the beginning of this book that the human frame could tolerate any speed but that it is susceptible to acceleration. There would be absolutely no point in reaching Mach 15 if it was necessary to commence deceleration immediately the maximum speed had been attained. Some sustained flight at maximum speed would be the only justification for the fantastic fuel consumption involved so the acceleration and deceleration times need to be fairly short if full advantage of the maximum speed is to be taken. A few figures will show that this is where the difficulty lies.

Most people have had the experience of being in a bus which had to make an emergency stop. The deceleration involved is of the order of 0.25 G and very few passengers enjoy the experience. Suppose a similar acceleration and deceleration force was used at the start and finish of a Mach 15 flight. It would be distinctly unpleasant.

Assume, however, that the passengers would be willing to accept a continuous acceleration equivalent to that of an emergency bus stop. It would take about half an hour to reach cruising speed and the same time to decelerate, one hour in all. Some 5,000 miles would be covered during this period of extreme discomfort, leaving 7,500 to be flown at maximum speed, just three quarters of an hour. Halve the acceleration and work at 0.125 G, probably an acceptable figure to most passengers, it would take an hour to reach cruising speed and 5,000 miles would be covered. Another hour to decelerate, covering another 5,000 miles. That would leave just 15 minutes flying at maximum speed, a completely ridiculous situation.

It is extremely dangerous to make any prophecies about the future of aviation but unless someone can find a means of making the human frame insensitive to acceleration forces—without making the passenger unconscious or putting him in a state of suspended animation in a deep freeze—it does look as if Mach 15, or anything near it, is quite impracticable for airline use on this earth. If we lived on Jupiter or Saturn it would be another matter but such a suggestion rather stretches into the realms of science fiction.

No one has ventured to express an opinion about the running costs of an airliner at such speeds but it may be possible to make an inspired guess. The Concord, scheduled for Mach 2.2, will carry 174,000 lb. of fuel for the Atlantic flight, including reserves. For a flight three and a half times as long it would have to carry about 600,000 lb. for the same speed. The proposed speed is more than six times greater so it would certainly be safe to say that the fuel consumption would be at least three times as great per hour or per mile and probably a lot worse than that. But if we stick at the optimistic three times this would involve lifting 1.8 million lb. of fuel off the ground and, if we hold to the same ratio of overall weight to fuel weight as applies in the Concord, the take-off weight of the Mach 15 airliner would be of the order of 3.3 million lb.—1,500 tons. And designing an airframe of that size would be a headache in itself.

Coming back to the fuel question there is more to it than just first cost, which might be about one shilling per gallon—a very rough guess be it said. The fuel has to be carried through the air and this costs money in itself. At the time of writing it costs a shipper about 11 shillings per lb. to send freight from London to New Zealand. This presumably includes a profit margin so the actual cost might be estimated at eight shillings per lb. In general terms the Mach 15 airliner will take off with full tanks and land with empty ones, less the statutory reserve fuel.

An average of half the take-off fuel will therefore be flown the full journey, i.e. 900,000 lb. *Carriage* of this load at current freight rates alone will cost the airline £360,000 for a single flight from London to Christchurch! If the fuel cost at the hypothetical one shilling per gallon is added, this will amount to an extra £11,000-odd. So, if this very large airliner carries between 350 and 400 passengers, as it well might, the fuel costs per passenger alone amount to about £1,000 before any account is taken of capital cost of the aircraft, crew costs, sales costs, advertising, airport charges, maintenance, etc., and, of course, profit. And this further assumes that the Mach 15 airliner will make at least two round trips a day, carrying 700 to 800 passengers a day in each direction. Such loads will probably never be achieved but even if they are each passenger will—on these assumed figures—have to pay a fare in the region of £2,000 for the single journey! Whatever else may be false in this look at the future it is absolutely certain that only the millionaires of this world will be willing to pay such prices for the saving of a few hours—and experience a lot of physical discomfort in doing so.

No doubt the designers will say that these figures are far worse than will be achieved in practice and they may be able to give chapter and verse in support of such a claim. Even so, if the estimate given is four times worse than the actual costs envisaged, a single fare of £500 would be needed and it is more than doubtful if a total of 1,600 passengers could be found every day who would want to travel between England and New Zealand or any comparable route even if the price was cut by a further 50 per cent. And the Mach 15 aircraft could only be used for very long haul operations. Even across the Atlantic it could never attain full speed without using accelerations far beyond those acceptable to the average human being.

This excursion into figures may well have been exaggerated but it does suggest that no civil use is ever likely to be made of a Mach 15 aircraft, or, indeed, an aircraft with anything like that speed. It may be that Dr. Wallis is right when he claims that nothing short of Mach 5 will be an economic proposition. It also looks quite probable that nothing much in excess of Mach 5 will ever be either economic or practicable—or both.

It was admitted earlier in this chapter that there was a lot of guesswork involved in looking so far ahead and the author certainly makes no claim to infallibility. Nevertheless, common-sense seems to suggest that there is a limit to the speeds that man can usefully attain when travelling round the surface of his own planet. Out in space and flying round the surfaces of other planets the situation may be entirely different and he would be a self-assured prophet indeed who said that these very high velocities will never have a place in man's transportation systems. But not while everyday man remains earthbound as most of us will for a long time yet.

HYPOTHETICAL SST FLIGHT

THE opinions of the airline pilots regarding the actual performance of an SST flight over the Atlantic are probably the most important contributions to this phase of commercial flight at a time when the designs are still to some degree in a fluid state and plans for effective air traffic control methods are in the making.

It was therefore very generous of the British Air Line Pilots Association—acting for the International Federation of Air Line Pilots' Associations—to give me facilities to make a verbatim report of the speeches made by a group of very experienced pilots from several countries and of the brief discussion which followed.

It will be seen that a great deal of very serious thought went into the preparation of these hypothetical descriptions of the various sectors of the flight but there was no lack of humour in the presentation. In

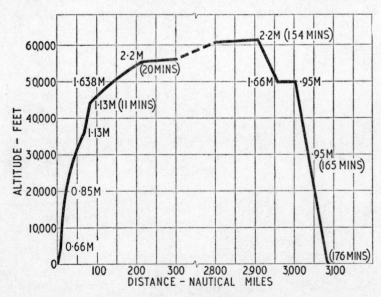

A typical Atlantic SST flight

Chapter 17 some comments on the qualities of the men who will fly the SSTs were offered. This appendix should give some idea of the kind of people they actually are.

THE AIRCRAFT—CAPTAIN F. ANDREANI

I MUST first of all present you with the supersonic transport of tomorrow as far as its general concept is concerned and its flight characteristics are concerned. It is a very difficult task, especially after having heard the experts who have spoken in the course of these last two days.

First of all, it is superfluous for me, before such an audience, to recall that when a passenger buys a ticket he has the right to expect that he shall be carried in conditions of complete safety. Undoubtedly this has been made obvious in this Symposium. Safety, regularity and comfort of passengers are the essential rules which will be applied to the SST.

Next in my picture of SST operations I would like to present the crew; I think that it should be made up of at least three members, and probably four. Going round the aircraft with the crew, we can see that the span is smaller than that of a subsonic aircraft and that the length is roughly the same; it has four jets; the landing gear will certainly be of a classical type, of a size perhaps to remind us that, at touch-down, the head of the pilot will be 45 feet above the runway. This, however, is a problem which the pilots will easily be able to solve.

Entering the aircraft, I will begin with the passenger cabin. There will be about 100 passengers, perhaps more. In the cockpit, what is of interest to us is the field of visibility. In my opinion it will be at least equal to that of present aircraft. The controls should not make it difficult to read the instrument panel. We hope that they will have direct contact with the surfaces, without perhaps there having to be any electronic correction, and that they will be designed in such a way that, whatever may be the system of transmission used, the displacement of the control surface will be proportional to that of the corresponding cockpit control movement.

If we look at the instrument panel it will certainly be smaller than in subsonic aircraft. We can see that the nose is a very sharp one and we hope that the instruments will be there in duplicate. As Captain Masland said this morning, we hope that this will leave room to put a pencil down somewhere.

As to the flight characteristics, they are the result of the general planning and design. Almost all the projects which we know, such as the Concord, envisage modified delta wings with a low aspect ratio.

In spite of their implied advantages some pilots are not very warmly in favour of variable geometry wings, because of the technological difficulties involved and also because of possible failure, but in any case we do not know, at the present moment, of any tangible proposals for aircraft of this type.

In the immediate future we shall have to deal with the heavy drag resulting from delta wings of low aspect ratio which may give very great difficulties from the point of view of flying. However, perhaps we are exaggerating these difficulties somewhat and our test pilot friends who have the experience of this type of delta wing have told us that these difficulties can be overcome fairly easily after a certain period of adaptation.

We must remember the time when jets were first introduced amid all the various scarecrows that were brandished at that time. We hope that the aircraft which is promised to us, whether it looks like the Concord or another, will be a good one, pleasant to fly, thanks to its aerodynamic design qualities and not because of little black boxes which may, perhaps, be superfluous.

We have been promised a simple aeroplane; we hope that this is true; that the systems that will be used will be conventional rather than revolutionary ones. We think that there will be enough difficulties as it is with the SST formula in itself; other novelties should be introduced progressively. We also think that most of the difficulties will be overcome but we don't want to indulge in either excessive optimism or excessive pessimism, and it is only when the aircraft has actually been put into service that we can draw proper conclusions; in any event we can, I think, come to one conclusion this week here in London . . . Wait and see.

HYPOTHETICAL SST FLIGHT
PRE-FLIGHT BRIEFING—CAPTAIN A. SPOONER

I would like to thank the first gentleman who called this high-speed vehicle an SST, a Supersonic Transport, for it certainly has crossed my mind as to whether or not this thing is an aircraft.

One of the great advantages of a Mach 1 aircraft is that, if you are thinking in terms of speed, Mach 1 is approximately 1,000 feet per second at a representative temperature; and, if my mathematics are correct, this means that Mach 2.2 is 2,200 feet per second and Mach 3 is 3,000 feet per second.

Having a friend in the War Office, I thought I would make some comparisons with certain well-known weapons and he writes to me as follows: the muzzle velocity of the Mk. 303, the standard army rifle, is 2,400 feet per second; that of the 40 millimetre anti-aircraft is 2,600 feet per second; that of the 3.7 heavy ack-ack is 2,800 feet per second —this, incidentally, made me rather favour the Mach 3, in case one gets in the wrong area—and the muzzle velocity of the 17-pounder anti-tank, armour-piercing V.C. (whatever that stands for) is 3,000 feet per second. Now, compared with SST speeds of up to 3,000 feet per second for Mach 3, these are quite interesting figures and it certainly makes me wonder whether we are dealing with an aircraft, a missile, or a projectile!

I have been asked to look after the flight planning section of this flight and whilst I have done my best to envisage the flight planning for a hypothetical flight from London to New York in the year 1971 (actually the flight was planned in 1970), it is greatly straining my powers of perception to attempt such a difficult task as flight planning the SST. It has to be admitted that this is no more than a cock-shy, submitted in part to provoke discussion, a discussion from which I, for one, would hope to learn. I trust, therefore, that the experts ranged before me will not hesitate to contradict.

I now take you to Flight Number 509, London to New York, 14 November 1971, scheduled departure time at 11.00 a.m.

It is, as the Irishmen say, a fine soft morning as I drive to the airport. It's raining cats and dogs, and grey clouds are swirling around the top of the control tower.

I report to the operations room at 8.30, some two and a half hours before departure. This has been made necessary ever since A.T.C. requirements (incidentally I think it should be A.T.C. services—the services are often left out in my opinion) were altered so that they insist upon being given complete flight details at least two hours before the SST departure.

At the airport I meet my crew—almost the same Crew that Captain Andreani put in the aircraft. It consists of a co-pilot holding an A.L.T.P. which, like my own, is an ordinary A.L.T.P. endorsed with the type; and a third pilot holding a commercial licence, similarly endorsed.

The co-pilot is specifically in charge of the communication and navigational systems and the third pilot is specifically in charge of engineering, electrical and electronic systems. However, this is a fail-safe crew in that all three of us have been trained to each other's specific tasks, and we are regularly checked out on these tasks.

Together we proceed to the met. bureau—or should I say weather office—where after checking that the forecast for Idlewild is above company minima and that I have an alternate airfield—Boston in this case—forecasting better than 800 feet cloud base and two miles forward visibility, I briefly study the 100 millibar and 50 millibar charts, noting that a weak, westerly flow exists. At a glance, this wind seems unlikely to affect the flight plan beyond about 3 per cent. I pay far more attention to the temperatures and I study the isotherms both around the 35,000-foot level and at the upper levels, 50,000 and beyond. Incidentally, it is only a small point, but the temperatures I now notice are printed in degrees Absolute. And since the temperature at 35,000 feet is fairly normal, say 221 degrees Absolute, I decide the flight plan and flight profile so that I will accelerate beyond Mach 0.9 (I think someone called it a transonic dash this morning) at 35,000 feet whilst over the Irish Sea, using the special transition corridor T.C.3 extending north-westwards in a curve from the Welsh coast. For obvious reasons it takes you out through the gap between Ireland and Scotland just in case you are having a bit of temperature trouble. I elect to take the special airways from London Airport, to the point off the Welsh coast where the transonic corridor begins.

I can now estimate my preliminary fuel requirements and I do this by adding together the following components; taxi fuel, take-off fuel, climb fuel to Flight Level 350, cruise fuel to the Welsh coast, transition fuel (at 55,000 lbs.—this is nearly one-third of the total fuel requirement), climb fuel to optimum altitude, climb-cruise fuel to point of descent, descent fuel, circuit and landing fuel. I total all this up and I add on 10 per cent under the heading of Provisional Contingency Reserve. Note the word "Provisional".

I then calculate my diversion fuel as being the fuel from Idlewild to Boston, cruising at the subsonic Flight Level of 330 and I finally add on 45 minutes holding and stand-off fuel, calculated at Flight Level 300.

My two pilots and I now proceed to the Geophysical Forecast room where, on closed circuit T.V. wall charts, we can study the daily forecast of ozone and radiation conditions for the magnetic latitudes appropriate to our chosen height and track.

Right, Handley Page 115 test vehicle used to examine the low-speed characteristics of the slender delta wing for the Concord; *below*, a photographic impression, based on a model, of the Concord in flight

Top, the variable-geometry-wing Boeing airliner designed for operation at speeds faster than 1,800 mph; *centre*, the Lockheed double-delta design for a Mach 3 airliner: the movable nose is intended to expand the pilot's field of vision; *below*, a model of the Russian SST, still more or less an unknown quantity. It bears a marked similarity to the Concord and Lockheed

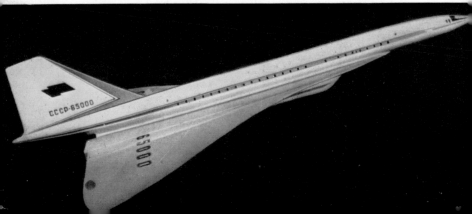

Whilst in the geophysical room we get the pretty little girl, the laboratory assistant in the white coat, to check our personal radiation film badges and to verify from her records that none of us is approaching any of the absorption limits. I notice incidentally that she takes a particularly keen interest in the film badge of my youthful and virile third pilot, whose Christian names appear to be "John, dear".

Next the co-pilot and I satisfy ourselves that the aircraft will be able to comply with the take-off requirements. We use the usual parameters of runway length, barometric pressure, temperature (still in Absolute), surface wind and runway slope, and additionally we apply the friction factors, that is to say the braking co-efficient and the wetness factor.

Having satisfied myself on this point, I now file my A.T.C. flight plan, specifying on this the time, location and height for my transonic acceleration, also the time, location and height for my point of transonic deceleration. I also specify an optimum cruise-climb throughout. A.T.C. promise to let me have a reply within ten minutes, and during this interval I drink the second of my pre-breakfast cups of coffee. In all, before I actually got breakfast in San Francisco, I drank eleven of these.

The A.T.C. clearance, after some ten minutes or so, duly comes back. This does not fully comply with all my requests. A.T.C. advise me that my start-up time will be Schedule + 06 minutes and that whilst the track is generally approved—actually I asked for Westerly Track Number 11 and got Westerly Track Number 12, but that is good enough—I will have to step-climb, commencing at Flight Level 430 over Belfast, climbing to 470 at 20 West, 550 at 45 West and 630 over Gander. Thereafter, at the time when I am interested in descent, I am cleared to step-climb. Furthermore, I am required to start descent ten minutes earlier than planned. This kind of clearance is quite normal for this particular flight owing to the fact that 18 other competitive airlines also wish to arrive at New York at the same time, approximately 8.30 in the morning.

Experience tells me that I should be able to adjust my speed to the amended westerly track, as I am keeping in reserve Mach 0.15 for this very purpose.

A printed copy of my A.T.C. clearance and my start-up time is given to me. I now feed the details of this clearance into an automatic computer, into which I had earlier fed my optimum flight plan requirements, and within 15 seconds a printed slip informs me that, due to A.T.C. clearance requirements, the flight time will now be 2 hours

13—SF

and 28 minutes instead of the 2 hours and 21 minutes which I had planned, and that my additional fuel requirement, due to A.T.C. changes, will be slightly over 6,342 lbs.

This figure is now added to the flight plan fuel requirement, under the heading of "A.T.C. fuel". Using the same automatic computer, which has by now stored and memorised details of my actual A.T.C. clearance, I select 5° against a "Temperature Increase" control gauge and learn, again within 15 seconds, that a 5° increase in temperature throughout will result, in my particular case, in an additional 7.3 per cent of fuel requirements. This 7.3 per cent additional fuel is now added to the flight plan and is compared with the actual contingency reserve of 10 per cent which was initially applied. This fuel is sometimes called "Temperature Variation Reserve".

The automatic computer adds the information that, for this particular flight, after-burning will not be required.

The estimated traffic load is now given me and I am in a position to calculate the accelerate-stop distance (using the wet runway case) and the take-off distance and lift-off speed, taking special care to ensure that the lift-off speed is within the I.C.A.O. laid down maximum of 160 knots, commonly referred to as "the Halaby Halt Point" and, in I.C.A.O., as Newton's Fifth Law.

The latest actual runway weather conditions are being continuously and automatically recorded on the walls of the briefing room and these enable me to check that visibility is still within my departure limits and that the maximum crosswind component of 30 knots is not likely to be exceeded.

I now proceed to the data recording room where I can study the printed engineering details of the preceding flight for my particular aircraft. These have been produced by the multi-parameter flight recorder tape carried on board. The third pilot and I take particular note of those components which are approaching their predetermined limits. These systems will receive his special attention during flight.

It is now departure time minus one hour and we proceed to the aircraft where we observe the refuelling. The fuel is a special kind of kerosene, since it has to meet a level of purity hitherto not demanded by other engines. It also contains additives to give it higher b.t.u. per pound of fuel, low volatility and low vapour pressures.

Before refuelling, the fuel temperatures for the last flight were carefully studied, again using the flight recorder trace, in order to check that the fuel had not exceeded the temperatures where fuel degradation would become a problem; and after refuelling we observe that the tanks are pressurised with an inert gas.

External checks are now made, but these are rather difficult to accomplish since the fuselage is way above our heads. However, out of habit, I reach up to give an affectionate pat to the convergent-divergent nozzles above my head. I give this pat because it is these convergent-divergent nozzles which, in their latest form, enable the aircraft to be climbed out without any noise abatement procedures, thus stopping three industrial disputes and a special I.C.A.O. meeting—but costing BALPA £500!

However, to compensate for the physical difficulties of checking, the third pilot activates his pre-flight check switch and an automatic check-out machine attached to the ground power unit completes the external check and also starts running through the internal, before-starting-engine, checks. This latter the pilots will also cross-check after the machine, using the normal verbal check list. After this second check the engine start-up interlock will be tested to make certain that all the items have been completed. This is necessary since no engine can, in fact be started unless all the checks satisfy this automatic interlock. This check out also ensures that ground delays due to last-minute maintenance defects will not delay the previously given start-up time.

Whilst in the aircraft I take another sample of the New York and Boston weather situation, using for this purpose the weather data teleprinter which relays actual and two-hour forecast reports from across the Atlantic via one of the U.H.F. communication satellites.

Once in my seat, I pull out the portable flight desk and I attach to this the A.T.C. printed coded clearance, the latest weather strip as it emerges from the teleprinter, and the terminal area map clearly showing my coded departure route. This route is also superimposed on the face of my pictorial navigational display system, and I mark it with a china-graph pencil. I am able to keep a visual check upon the weather, thanks to the water-repellant system already clearing my windscreen.

I now settle down in my seat, fasten my lap strap, secure my shoulder harness and, since this is the end of my particular part of the flight, I let Captain Bateman start my engines.

TAKE-OFF AND CLIMB—CAPTAIN F. H. BATEMAN

HAVING got clearance to start we can start the thing up. I imagine there is going to be a little bit of a problem of jet blast as usual, but this is obviously going to be a matter for the Airport Authorities rather than for the pilot. Taxying out, I imagine the residual thrust is sufficient and we may have to be rather careful of the brakes. The fact that we are not able to see the wing tips probably at this point is not important since it has a narrow span, but the length of this thing is going to make it be a little bit difficult taxying because I think we are going to be about 50 feet in front of the nose wheel and 100 feet in front of the main gear and it is going to cut out a lot of these rather tight little corners we have to go round at the moment.

We would be cleared, presumably rather quickly, to at least the holding position. From the conversation this morning it looks as though we will still have a little problem actually getting on to the runway, and then once again off it.

The actual take-off, once cleared, will be slightly difficult because the power available presumably will preclude running up to full power on the brakes. This means that the power will have to be applied after one has started to roll and this will mean a certain amount of time scatter in the application of take-off power. A pleasant problem here possibly might be the setting of take-off power which may be less than the maximum. Normally everybody gets at the throttles and pushes and waits to get off the ground; with the SST depending, of course, on the individual design of the aircraft. Every time we take off we have at least to consider that we may have to abandon it a short way down and the problems here will be slightly different: the acceleration will be much greater than—at least we hope it will be much greater than—the present-day subsonic jets; so the point at which one will need to abandon the take-off will be noticeably earlier. The actual engine failure problem will possibly revolve around the time it takes the pilot to recognise he has a power loss and to take action to remedy this. This may merely mean setting up extra power on the other three engines.

The runway surface will be a problem just the same as it is today and no doubt there will have to be a considerable amount of experimentation and proving to our satisfaction that the aircraft we are flying can handle a certain amount of water on the runway, a certain amount of snow and a certain amount of slush.

Before we actually move off, I should mention here that the fact that we cannot see anything of the wing in all probability means that we will probably need some sort of inspection ability for the wing surfaces. As somebody pointed out, it is not always V.R.F., we sometimes get a bit of snow, and the time taken to get take-off

clearance may be sufficient for us to collect snow on the aircraft. We
have to have some method by which we can inspect it before we
actually start rolling and it is obviously going to be highly desirable if
we can also inspect the operation of the control surfaces. We are
going to have to rely on elevons, presumably; on this particular type
it will be a little late to see if they are working just as we leave the
ground—or not.

Assuming that we have all these things—we have checked the aircraft
as clear and we start to roll; the performance is much the same, and
we will have agreed between ourselves from a bunch of graphs that
we are to commence rotation at a certain speed. This rotation speed—
shall we say "rotation point" for the moment—will be earlier than it
is to-day because the angle through which we will have to rotate will
be greater, the time taken to rotate, even if it is not longer, will
certainly allow more acceleration because the rate of acceleration is
greater. We are flying a type of aircraft in which the elevators are
rather insensitive compared with those of present aircraft with a
separate tail and too much elevator displacement substantially increases
drag and gives another problem. So you can see that this is going to
have to be thought out rather closely and that rotation will have to be
done just right. It will also have to be done to just the right angle.

Mr. Hall yesterday mentioned that quite often a pilot under-rotates
and also hesitates during the rotation. This has a much greater penalty
for any delta-form aircraft—I am having to assume that we are operating
a delta-form of some description at the moment.

The necessity for this accurate rotation to an accurate angle highlights the great desirability of having a reliable take-off flight director.
The amount of nose-up angle which will be applied will leave one with
very little other than side visibility; so a considerable amount of
practical background work will presumably have been done when we
are sitting in this thing, rotating it, to give us a correct rotation angle
so that we can clear the ground somewhere near where we should do.

Once we are off the ground our problems somewhat decrease.
Of course, flying is always a little tricky; you know what an aeroplane
is—it's a thing which very nearly doesn't fly—and we are going to have
this problem: once we have got it into the air of having to keep it up
there.

I am sure that, having got it off the ground, we will have a noise
abatement procedure in the airport terminal area. (Of course, this
becomes Noisy Bateman if I am involved personally!) But in any event

we are not going to have anything easy, like just pointing it West and off we go. There is going to be a certain amount of low-to-middle-level turning possibly with reduced power for noise abatement. I am not in favour of this but I am afraid that this is the way it is going to be.

Once clear of the terminal area we will be cleared fairly rapidly, I think, to 25,000 feet. This is a good move.

Continuing the climb, one is obviously going to have to fly this thing subsonically up to about 40,000 feet, or maybe a little bit above, to avoid complaints arising from boom.

At about the tropopause one reaches one of the best areas, presumably, for going supersonic. One climbs fairly rapidly when cleared, at some 25,000 feet a minute, to the tropopause and one will have to manoeuvre to a predetermined area set aside for transition to supersonic flight. In this area one will level off, presumably rather cautiously with that rate of climb and, when so cleared, proceed to go transonic.

Just below Mach 1, one comes up against considerable drag rise and this area of high drag lasts from roughly Mach 0.9 or 0.95 to about Mach 1.2 to 1.3. If the design of the aircraft is such that it does not have a great excess of power, this transonic area may take some time. Exactly what time I cannot at the moment estimate, but the time taken in going transonic will also depend on temperature. These are problems which I cannot handle at the moment; we just have to have them demonstrated and hope they are fixed by the time we really have to do this regularly. But higher temperatures do pose the problem that available engine power is reduced and the transonic time will be stretched somewhat. What the effect of this is on the rest of the flight will obviously have to be known before departure, and suitable reserves will have to be taken.

Having accelerated to beyond Mach 1.3, the aircraft will depart from stabilised level flight—incidentally this stabilised level flight obviously has to be fully approved by A.T.C. We will not be able to undertake any manoeuvring at that point—and we change to a cruise-climb. The rate of climb here (somewhere between 500 and 5,000 feet per minute) will depend largely on the aircraft design, and the cruise-climb will continue possibly up to somewhere about 60,000 feet, where the design cruise speed will be attained.

The problems of the flight are greatly diminished once one has reached the cruise speed and at this point my own problems diminish, because I am going to hand over to Captain Masland.

CRUISE—CAPTAIN W. M. MASLAND

I HAVE had crew changes in many places in my life but this is the first time I have had a crew-change at 60,000 feet! There have been various comments about drift-up; it is my impression that, in relation to previous operations, this is a negligible feature, but there may be a saving of something like 3 per cent by using drift-up technique. This sounds like a small figure, something in the nature of a return on a Government Bond, but this is 3 per cent, I presume, of the all-up fuel and, when translated into passenger revenue, you have an entirely different problem, something like £3,000 (revenue pounds) for one size aeroplane, £6,000 for another one.

I would like to remind you that civil aviation is the art of supporting yourself in the air—financially! It appears to me that the pressure will be on for drift-up technique. Of course, there is nothing new about it; twenty to twenty-five years ago we used it. On one particular flight where we had a good chance to calibrate the aircraft—and each aircraft was different in those days—we took off with a war overload, levelled off at 1,000 feet, set the angle of attack (through the air speed indicator) at what corresponded to the maximum L/D and in 40 minutes we had drifted down to 250 feet. It took another six hours to drift back up again to 1,000 and then several more hours to get up to 8,000 feet where we wanted to be in the middle of the flight. From that giddy altitude we had good celestial navigation.

The point is that there are what appear to be minor economies which, on a marginal aircraft, and I think this aircraft will be marginal financially, will make a great difference. To go back to an old technique we had an aircraft once that, for certification to meet the advertised high speed, had offset the vertical fin. Of course, the figure for maximum speed was of no value to us and the modification meant that we had to crank in rudder trim at cruise speed. As soon as we got to the lower weight where we could begin to pull back power for long range cruise, some pilots started pulling back power on number 4 engine first, by this means cranking out the rudder trim and gaining another knot or two out of it. By these techniques we were able to up our payload 25 per cent.

If the SST is a marginal aircraft financially, all of these techniques, or ones similar, applicable to this type of machine, will be put into play. In large part this will call for a high degree of freedom in the vertical plane, and this in turn will call for a disposition of the air space in such a way that this can be accomplished. To me this means precise lateral separation. I do not believe that we will need too many tracks in even the high density areas, such as the North Atlantic. If the SST aircraft are fired off in rapid succession the tube can be kept full and one need have only another parallel emergency track for aircraft that get into trouble. Something of this sort may be feasible. It does call for precise navigation in the lateral plane and, it would appear to me, a high degree of freedom in the vertical plane.

A question arises as to what happens if you lose the fire in one of the boilers. It was said that you might have to go subsonic to re-light. This means, perhaps, that you may have to dip down and if so, how do you have a track of your own in the vertical plane?

After you have gone down and re-lit, do you have the fuel to go back supersonic? These are some questions which I would like to pass on.

As far as cockpit design is concerned, this is going to make a very great deal of difference in every aspect of the flight including the cruise phase. I would like, hopefully, to make one more plea for a cockpit which will be a more workable command centre for the aircraft. I think that it is possible that we may have to accept fully powered controls and if this is so, why not have a side stick; once you remove the wheel and the yoke, you have an immediate capability for much better presentation.

I am sure that there are any number of en route problems that have been touched on through the sessions that have not been covered, some that we may not uncover until the first flights. However at this point I would like to hand over to Captain Taylor to get the aircraft down.

DESCENT AND LANDING—CAPTAIN L. TAYLOR

THE moment when I start accepting responsibility for this aircraft I have a real problem—acquisition of information. How goes the flight? How far do I have to go? How long will it take to get there— 10 minutes, 35 minutes? How much fuel is left? Nearly all the fuel Tony Spooner elected to carry is gone. Will I use computers? I hope so; there is enough to do without doing basic arithmetic.

What about the terminal condition? The weather, the service-ability of the facilities at the field; is there snow on the runway? (They fixed me, didn't they—we're doing this flight in the winter-time to New York.) What is the serviceability of the aircraft equipment?

I also need prior notification of the approach tracks and the runway in use at my destination. How shall I obtain this information? Distance to go? I hope I am going to obtain it from the long anticipated IFALPA dream—a pictorial area-coverage navigational aid.

What is the fuel remaining? I need much better fuel consumption and quantity measuring systems. The importance of the aircraft clock as a precise measuring device must be reduced. Is there any change in the terminal conditions? I am far too busy to handle voice communications referring to such routine information, which must be automated and given to me in a recorded form, so reducing flight-deck workload; radio-teletype is an obvious candidate for this task.

How about the aircraft serviceability? The vital systems which I am about to use, such as auto-pilot couplers, radio-altimeters, flight instruments, navigational radios, etc., must all have a self-test facility which is meaningful. I am already disenchanted with those warning light type pilot-tranquillisers, and so are many of my colleagues.

The most vital items must be self-monitored and multiplexed as necessary. Should they become unserviceable at a later stage I demand warning systems that cannot be overlooked.

I need the right crew composition to help me gain and evaluate vital information. There can be no semi-inactive crew members in this, the busiest stage of flight.

Air traffic control must not expect me to make last-minute improvisations in my approach profile. At the optimum time I wish to descend, not to be told to maintain my altitude and then later to expedite my descent. Having reached the decision that the time to descend is now, I have to set up the descent. For this I need instrumentation not yet available. The aircraft at this stage, I believe, has no performance problems, but we may now be running into an area of handling problems.

If I close the throttles completely can I be assured that I have no pressurisation, air conditioning and, later on, no engine anti-icing problems? I do not know the answer, but perhaps someone among the panel will inform me.

How can I accurately control my descent? Assuming that we commence descent from, say, 70,000 feet, I expect that I shall have to descend to, say, 45,000 feet still supersonic and avoiding, by carrying this speed, what has been picturesquely described previously as coffin corner. I must have adequate margins above the minimum in-flight speeds to give me good handling. Tight auto-pilot control is a must.

These are the things I need on the auto-pilot: I need altitude hold; I need Mach hold; I need indicated air-speed hold; I need vertical speed hold; I need attitude hold; I need smooth manoeuvre capability; I need reliable and, if necessary, multiplexed auto-throttle systems, preferably using both processed angle of attack and air speed as references. These systems, if provided, should give me tight control of the aircraft, flight profile and velocity.

Meanwhile, some 100 feet behind and beneath me, Tom Frost's variable configuration power plants are behaving themselves, or not behaving themselves, as the case may be. If one of the power plants flames out, will I be able to re-light it at descent altitudes and speeds? If the auto control of engine configuration fails, what kind of increased work load will be imposed on the flight crew?

Meanwhile, back in the passenger cabin, we have achieved a floor angle of how many degrees? I do not know. Are the passengers already strapped in?

Now we are going to reach the tricky bit—the transition from supersonic to subsonic flight. I need an area free of significant turbulence. Shall I fly level to decelerate? Am I going to use airframe drag augmentation devices? I do not know. Can I use reverse thrust in the air? Perhaps.

Now assuming that I have achieved a subsonic state, I will take down my wind shield as recommended—I am flying at Mach 0.8 or 0.9. The ARB requirements and the FAA "Request for Proposals" have provided me with an aircraft with good handling characteristics which I am assured are different but no worse than the aircraft of which we have previous experience.

If the A.T.C. authorities have received the message from Captain Masland, I will not have to hold. However, when I do hold, I am back in the "acquisition of information" state again, fuel remaining, weather, etc., beginning to worry me. The aircraft is scheduled to leave on a return flight in one hour's time and an excessive time on the ground at the wrong airport for this aircraft will put my employer out of business.

It looks as though we are due to carry out an all-weather operations type landing. As the weather problem I face covers the whole area, I need two runways at different locations which are equipped and certificated for all-weather landing. If I divert, at what height and speed shall I divert?

Can I now check the performance of the aircraft component of the all-weather landing system. Once again, no tranquillisers, please. I must be sure. If all is O.K. I now continue the approach to the final fix.

What I do not need now, while the flight deck check list work is being done, is uninvited interruptions from the ground agencies. It is positively hazardous to interrupt these vital cockpit procedures, and this is one reason why navigation must be done from the flight deck. Give us the A.T.C. clearance, give us the navigational capability, and keep quiet, please. What kind of human performance is it reasonable to expect in a critical task if the pilot has to wear telephones and monitor an excess of communications?

I have now checked my all-weather landing system, I hope, and I hope that I have the kind of instrumentation advocated by other people. I need an improved flight director. I need the same information available to me as is available to the auto-pilot. I need tight auto-pilot coupling. I need tight auto-throttle control. I need good malfunction warning systems. The provision of adequate information to monitor progress of the flight profile, preferably with information from a source separate from that used by the auto-pilot plus, and this is a must, the ability directly to intervene at any time I so choose.

Now we must examine some of the handling problems of the SST in the approach and landing configurations. We have been promised, and expect to get: (i) moderate approach and landing speeds; (ii) crosswind landing capability up to 30 knots; and (iii) adequate power and good engine control. We have been told to expect to approach at speeds lower than the minimum drag speed; therefore we must have a good, reliable auto-throttle system. We are obviously going to be rather noisy. This is a problem for people other than the pilots to solve; there is a limit to the variation in flight path that we will be able to make. I estimate that we need a straight-in approach of up to ten miles in length with a glide slope angle of $2\frac{1}{2}$ degrees; and I do hope that the Idlewild Authorities are not going to request me to avoid over-flying the Jones Beach Outdoor Cinema because I am disturbing the patrons.

How about the engine-out approaches and landings? The engines will, we hope, achieve the splendid reliability of already existing jet engines. However, they are more powerful, a little more complex, and in the early stages of operation it would be surprising if there were no engine failures at all. What extra problems in handling will this produce? Will we have a problem in go-arounds? We know we will be using high power on approach on four engines; how much will we use on three, or even two? Will there always be power to accelerate to climb-out speeds?

Assuming that all goes well, we carry out an auto-pilot coupled approach using auto-throttle. Speed control is good, the approach is accurate. We cross the landing threshold at 130 knots at 35 ft. There is a cross-wind, there is wind shear, there is turbulence, there is sleet. (I ought not to be flying, really, ought I?) Is the windscreen clear; if so, it will be the first ever. Is the angle of field of view adequate for my task? Can I have a choice of manual landing, auto-flare, or full auto-land in the conditions I specify?

Are runways slippery and wet? My main wheels have just touched the ground; I myself am still 50 feet up in the air. How much of the landing distance will be lost in lowering the nose gear before I can use brakes and reverse thrust? Is the anti-skid system good? Is a tail parachute provided? Is runway arrester gear provided? Can I maintain the runway centre-line in the cross wind? The answer to all these questions has to be yes, but I hope that some panel members will supply somewhat fuller answers.

Now, having landed, we taxi the aircraft. As someone else has said, I can't see the wing tips, the wheel base is long, and I have to navigate, I suppose, the runway turn-offs, the taxiways and, that ever-present threat to a pilot's seniority, a congested parking area. Is engine-idle-power too much for the taxi speeds? Are wheel, brake and tyre temperature indications provided for? And finally, what is the fate of the fuel remaining in the aircraft tanks? Has it become unusable due to having served as a heat sink? These are questions which have to be resolved before the SST commences regular airline route flying.

HYPOTHETICAL SST FLIGHT
DISCUSSION

RANGE

Captain Nishigori (Japanese Airline Pilots' Association) said that Japanese and probably Australian interests called for a really long range SST, and asked whether there were any plans for the development of such an aircraft with a range up to 4,000 nautical miles.

Mr. White (North American Aviation) recalled that, when subsonic jets started, they had not the extremely long range that was required for carriers operating over the Pole to Tokyo or Los Angeles or other equally long routes, and he thought it reasonable to expect, after acquiring operating experience at the middle ranges, that additional models would be introduced capable of flying the long range routes. He said that sonic boom limitations provided a definite reason for keeping the weight of the aircraft down to the minimum that would do the job demanded of it, and the call was to increase the payload carrying capability and the range of SSTs without greatly increasing their weight and size.

THE FLIGHT DECK

Captain Bressey (British Air Line Pilots' Association) said that certain parts of the aircraft structure which projected into the cockpit were impossible to insulate thermally, and he referred particularly to the heavy structural members around the windscreen and side windows, and suggested that these might reach temperatures as hot as 120° C. during supersonic flight. He asked how this would affect the pilots.

Mr. Harpur (British Aircraft Corporation) replied that in fact no parts of the aircraft structure with which pilots would physically come in contact should be above 25–30° C. and that this applied to everything including the transparencies which would have cooling air passed through interspaces between the layers.

Captain Hill (British Air Line Pilots' Association) enquired, in view of obvious requirements for a functional flight deck layout, what design studies had been made of all the operational aspects of the pilot's work to ensure the most efficient flight deck operation.

Mr. Harpur said that it had been proposed that a work study should be carried out on the SST employing the knowledge of the airline pilots, with the object of providing a cockpit layout which was satisfactory to meet the demands of the flight. At the same time, although the cockpit space was small, they were not going to sacrifice safety in terms of making the cockpit even smaller.

A questioner from the floor asked at what point the heat shield should be raised.

Mr. Wilde (British Aircraft Corporation) said that, speaking from an aerodynamic point of view, the heat shield was something that was going to give a good supersonic cruise performance. He expected that it would not be raised until the aircraft reached about 40,000 feet, certainly above the normal heavy traffic levels of subsonic jets. At this altitude the aircraft would still be in the very low supersonic speed regime.

Mr. Tymczyszyn (Federal Aviation Authority) said that the American requirement called for adequate forward and sideways vision for all manoeuvres.

Mr. Harpur said that the pilot would always have some forward view possible through the side panels. The shield had been incorporated to improve the aerodynamic performance and was not really a heat shield at all; the side windows had been left clear and they got just as hot as the front.

Captain Nicholl (British Air Line Pilots' Association) asked why, if the visor was not a heat shield and was not carrying any structural or pressurising loads, a great deal more of it had not been made of glass.

Mr. Wilde replied that they were still experimenting and were anxious to obtain opinions on how much of the visor should be made of glass. On the Concord, he said, they were faced with a modified delta wing with a relatively high approach attitude, and they had to provide a field of view consistent with or better than present subsonic jets. This meant providing a lot of downward view relative to the axis of the aircraft and, if this view were to be provided with a conventional windscreen, it would require a long length of glass, involving big structural glazing problems, and rather small angles between the line of vision and the glass, which they considered would give rise to unacceptable aberrations in view. They preferred to resolve the problem by adhering to the conventional line-of-vision to glazing angles, and to deal with the aerodynamic problem by using a visor. The amount of vision to be provided through the visor was something which was still subject to discussion, and pilot opinions in this matter would be welcomed.

General Operational Problems

Mr. Tymczyszyn, dealing with the general operational problems raised by the Panel Chairmen in relation to their concept of an SST flight, said that he had some comments to make which would be factual statements based on current aircraft or research programmes at present under way.

During taxying the wingtips would not be visible unless the aircraft had variable sweep, but in many current jet transports with most satisfactory taxying records the pilots could not see the wing tips. The American "Request for Proposals" stated that the aircraft must be able to use existing runways so that taxying would follow the old pattern of taxying past the strip and then turning. Take-off acceleration would be greater, 100 knots being reached in about 14 seconds instead of the present 22–24 seconds. Rotation presented no great difficulty. The theoretical aero-dynamicist liked to worry about the loss of elevator effectiveness on a delta but, in fact, the elevator feel was just as good as on any present-day aircraft, and pilots who had flown many types of delta had not found rotation a difficulty. He thought that rotation techniques would be more predictable and more satisfying to pilots than in current aircraft, since they were not depending alone on flight directors; they were also depending on proper trim, on the genius of the designer of the aircraft and on the many things that were constantly being learned about how to take an aircraft off properly. It was quite possible that it would be made a requirement that the trim would be such that a normal take-off rotation would result in a satisfactory take-off performance.

With regard to noise abatement procedures, everything was being done to keep noise levels within tolerable limits, and this was part of their engine specification. It might well be that engine design would be dictated by the transonic acceleration on a hot day. If this were so, the thrust selected on take-off would be less than maximum, which would mean a relatively low noise level. Furthermore, loss of an engine during take-off would merely call for the advancing of the remaining lever or levers to provide the additional thrust required, and for the one-in-a-million occasions on which an engine was lost on take-off he was sure the community would not object to the increased noise level. He did not envisage any special noise abatement procedures.

With regard to ice accretion, he thought that the supersonic wing was generally regarded as better in this respect in adverse take-off conditions, since it was sharper and less prone to collect ice. He expected climb-out procedures that were entirely compatible with existing air traffic control systems. Many flight profiles had been flown in military Mach 2 aircraft at peak traffic times, and the principal cause of complaint from pilots had been the necessity for constant frequency changes. There seemed to be some general misunderstanding about levelling out in the tropopause for transonic acceleration. In the SST a high enough thrust-to-weight ratio was expected to enable the acceleration to be made in a slight climb, thereby minimising boom over-pressures. The rate of climb to transonic acceleration altitude would be roughly double that of present-day aircraft; climbing at a just subsonic speed, the aircraft would arrive at transonic acceleration altitude in 7 to 9 minutes, depending on weight. In transonic acceleration there was a relative drag rise up to Mach 1.3, after which the rate of climb would rise considerably. The climb to cruise altitude, ironically enough, would still take 20 minutes, whether in a subsonic or a supersonic aircraft. It was at this point, the levelling out smoothly at a selected altitude from the very high rate of climb, that a problem was posed.

Referring to engine re-starting capabilities, he said that the American requirement was for engine re-starting to be possible both in subsonic and supersonic flight.

Mr. Britton (Bristol-Siddeley), commenting on re-lighting in flight, said that he saw no technical difficulty in obtaining re-lighting in any phase of flight, without change of altitude or speed and, with a good air intake, there was no reason why this should not be achieved.

Captain Jamoulle (Belgian Air Line Pilots' Association) asked if it would be possible to use reverse thrust for in-flight purposes.

Mr. Wilde said it would be premature for any designer at this stage to say that reverse thrust could be used in flight; it was to be expected that the configuration would give the highest probability that this should be so, but they would not in fact rely on this feature. It was also thought that there would not be additional airframe drag-producing devices, and that the combined throttle, nozzle and intake controls would give all the control over the deceleration which would be needed in this phase.

Reverting to the general operational problems outlined by the five Panel Chairmen, Mr. Wilde referred first to aircraft noise on approach. On this he considered that the increase in complaints on the ground arose from compressor noise, particularly in the cases of some large front compressor face diameters with high tip speed. A possibility existed here, certainly on SSTs, of using the variable inlet geometry to choke off inlet noise, and exhaust noise was not expected to be a problem in this area.

With regard to residual fuel, there was no question on the Concord of degradation of fuel left in tanks following its usage as a heat sink. This might be a problem with other designs working at higher ram temperatures, but this was not a problem on the Concord.

FLYING CONTROLS

Captain Clark (American Air Line Pilots' Association) referring to fully-powered controls, said that he believed he spoke for a great number of pilots in saying that they were not ready to accept this concept at the present time. The system visualised appeared to be a combination of electric and hydraulic, and he had recently had the misfortune of experiencing an in-flight emergency which required the removal of all electrical power from the aircraft as well as of hydraulic power. He asked how, in circumstances such as these, it was envisaged that the aircraft would be flown.

There was no reply to this question from the platform, though a speaker from the floor said that there were many pilots at present quite happily flying aircraft with fully powered controls.

SPACIAL DISORIENTATION

Captain Rodgers (Canadian Air Line Pilots' Association) asked Dr. Bennett what he considered the effects of the flight on the crew would be from low humidity and spacial disorientation.

Dr. Bennett (B.O.A.C.) said that he did not think that disorientation was of very serious significance in civil aircraft. The more severe manifestations were virtually confined to pilots of high altitude single-seater military aircraft, due to a combination of physical and sensory isolation. The higher accelerations and comparative lack of visual reference in an SST with a windscreen visor down would increase the likelihood of disorientation, but should present no serious difficulties to experienced instrument pilots. Very low humidities were undesirable, though unlikely to be harmful in the anticipated exposure time. However, it was essential to ensure that the environmental conditions in flight were such that pilots would not suffer any ill effect either during one flight or during a whole series of flights.

AIRLINES WHICH HAVE ORDERED THE SST
(September 1965)

Airline	Concord	American SST
Aeronaves de Mexico		2
Air France	8	6
Air India	2	3
Alitalia		3
American Airlines	6	6
Braniff		2
B.O.A.C.	8	6
Canadian Pacific		3
Continental	3	
Delta		5
El Al		2
Iberia		3
Irish International		2
Japan Air Lines		5
K.L.M.	3	3
Lufthansa		3
Middle East	2	
North West		4
Pakistan International		2
Pan-American	6	15
Panagra		2
QANTAS	4	6
Trans American Aeronautical Agency		2
Trans-World Airlines	6	10
Total	**48**	**93**

Trans American Aeronautical Agency is a firm which will lease aircraft to other operators.

WORLD'S AIR SPEED RECORDS (LANDPLANES)

Pilot	Aircraft	Engine	Date	Speed m.p.h.
Santos-Dumont (Brazilian)	Santos-Dumont 14 bis	Antoinette	12.11.06	25.7
Henri Farman (French)	Voisin	Antoinette 50 H.P.	26.10.07	32.7
Tissandier (French)	Wright	Wright	20. 5.09	34.0
Curtiss (American)	Herring-Curtiss	Curtiss	24. 8.09	43.3
Blériot (French)	Blériot 42	Anzani	28. 8.09	46.1
Blériot (French)	Blériot	E.N.V.	28. 8.09	47.8
Latham (French)	Antoinette	Antoinette	23. 4.10	48.2
Morane (French)	Blériot	Gnôme	10. 7.10	66.1
Leblanc (French)	Blériot	Gnôme 100 H.P.	29.10.10	68.2
Leblanc (French)	Blériot	Gnôme	12. 4.11	69.4
Nieuport (French)	Nieuport	Nieuport	11. 5.11	74.4
Leblanc (French)	Blériot	Gnôme 100 H.P.	12. 6.11	77.7
Nieuport (French)	Nieuport	Nieuport	16. 6.11	80.8
Nieuport (French)	Nieuport	Nieuport	21. 6.11	82.7
J. Védrines (French)	Deperdussin	Gnôme 140 H.P.	13. 1.12	90.1

Pilot	Aircraft	Engine	Date	Speed m.p.h.
J. Védrines (French)	Deperdussin	Gnôme 140 H.P.	22. 2.12	100.2
J. Védrines (French)	Deperdussin	Gnôme 140 H.P.	29. 2.12	100.9
J. Védrines (French)	Deperdussin	Gnôme 140 H.P.	1. 3.12	103.6
J. Védrines (French)	Deperdussin	Gnôme 140 H.P.	2. 3.12	104.3
J. Védrines (French)	Deperdussin	Gnôme 140 H.P.	13. 7.12	106.1
J. Védrines (French)	Deperdussin	Gnôme 140 H.P.	9. 9.12	108.2
M. Prévost (French)	Deperdussin	Gnôme 160 H.P.	17. 6.13	111.7
M. Prévost (French)	Deperdussin	Gnôme 160 H.P.	27. 9.13	119.2
M. Prévost (French)	Deperdussin	Gnôme 160 H.P.	29. 9.13	126.6
Sadi-Lecointe (French)	Nieuport	Hispano-Suiza 300 H.P.	7. 2.20	171.0
Jean Casale (French)	Blériot	Hispano-Suiza 300 H.P.	28. 2.20	176.1
De Romanet (French)	Blériot-Spad 20	Hispano 300 H.P.	9.10.20	181.8
Sadi-Lecointe (French)	Nieuport	Hispano-Suiza 300 H.P.	10.10.20	184.3
Sadi-Lecointe (French)	Nieuport	Hispano-Suiza 300 H.P.	20.10.20	187.9
De Romanet (French)	Blériot-Spad 20	Hispano 300 H.P.	4.11.20	192.0
Sadi-Lecointe (French)	Nieuport	Hispano 300 H.P.	12.12.20	194.5
Sadi-Lecointe (French)	Nieuport-Delage	Hispano 300 H.P.	26. 9.21	205.2

Pilot	Aircraft	Engine	Date	Speed m.p.h.
Sadi-Lecointe (French)	Nieuport-Delage	Hispano 300 H.P.	21. 9.22	211.9
B. G. Mitchell (American)	Curtiss CD.12	374 H.P.	13.10.22	222.9
Sadi-Lecointe (French)	Nieuport-Delage	Hispano 300 H.P.	15. 2.23	233.0
R. L. Maughan (American)	Curtiss R.6	Curtiss 465 H.P.	29. 3.23	236.5
Lieut. Brow (American)	Curtiss D.12, C.1	300 H.P.	2.11.23	259.1
Lieut. Williams (American)	Curtiss Racer, R.2, C.1	Curtiss 500 H.P.	4.11.23	266.5
Adj. Bonnet (French)	Ferbois V.2	Hispano-Suiza 450 H.P.	11.12.24	278.4
J. H. Doolittle (American)	Gee Bee	Pratt and Whitney Wasp 800 H.P.	9. 9.32	294.4
J. R. Wedell (American)	Wedell-Williams	Pratt and Whitney Wasp Senior	4. 9.33	304.4
R. Delmotte (French)	Caudron C.460	Renault 380 H.P.	25. 9.34	314.3
Howard Hughes (American)	Hughes Special	Pratt and Whitney Wasp 1,000 H.P.	13. 9.35	352.3
H. Wurster (German)	B.F.113	D.B. 600 950 H.P.	11.11.37	379.6
H. Dieterle (German)	Heinkel He 112 V.	D.B. 601 1,175 H.P.	30. 3.39	463.9
F. Wendel (German)	Messerschmitt Bf. 109 R.	D.B. 601	26. 4.39	469.2

Pilot	Aircraft	Engine	Date	Speed m.p.h.
G/C Wilson (British)	Gloster Meteor IVEE 454	2 Rolls-Royce Derwent Turbo-jet	7.11.45	606.3
G/C Donaldson (British)	Gloster Meteor IVEE 549	2 Rolls-Royce Derwent Turbo-jet	7. 9.46	615.99
Col. Boyd (American)	Lockheed P.80. R.	Allison J.33.A.21 Turbo-jet	4. 6.47	623.7
T. F. Caldwell (American)	Douglas Skystreak	T.G. 180 Turbo-jet 4,000 lb. thrust	20. 8.47	640.7
M. E. Carl (American)	Douglas Skystreak	T.G. 180 Turbo-jet 4,000 lb. thrust	25. 8.47	650.9
R. L. Johnson (American)	North American F.86 Sabre	General Electric J.47 Turbo-jet	15. 9.48	670.9
J. S. Nash (American)	North American F.86 Sabre	General Electric J.47.17 Turbo-jet	19.11.52	698.5
W. F. Barns (American)	North American F.86 Sabre	G.E. J.47.17 Turbo-jet	16. 7.53	715.7
Neville Duke (British)	Hawker Hunter	Rolls-Royce Avon R.A.7. Turbo-jet	7. 9.53	727.6
M. Lithgow (British)	Vickers Supermarine Swift	Rolls-Royce Avon R.A.7 Turbo-jet	25. 9.53	735.7

Pilot	Aircraft	Engine	Date	Speed m.p.h.
J. Verdin (American)	Douglas	Westinghouse J.40. WE.8 Turbo-jet	3.10.53	752.9

ALL THE FOLLOWING RECORDS WERE SUPERSONIC (IRRESPECTIVE OF HEIGHT)

Pilot	Aircraft	Engine	Date	Speed
F. Everest (American)	North American F.100 Supersabre	Pratt and Whitney J.57.7 Turbo-jet	29.10.53	773.7
H. A. Hanes (American)	North American F.100 Supersabre	Pratt and Whitney J.57.P Turbo-jet	20. 8.55	822.2
L. P. Twiss (British)	Fairey Delta 2	Rolls-Royce Avon Turbo-jet	10. 3.56	1,132.1
A. E. Drew (American)	McDonnel	Pratt and Whitney J.57 Turbo-jet	12.12.57	1,207.3
W. Irwin (American)	Lockheed F.104	G.E. J.79 Turbo-jet	16. 5.58	1,404.0
G. Mossolov (Russian)	E.66	TRD RS.7.F Turbo-jet	31.10.59	1,483.7
J. W. Rogers (American)	Convair F.106A Delta Dart	Pratt and Whitney J.75.P.17 Turbo-jet	15.12.59	1,525.9
R. B. Robinson (American)	McDonnell Phantom	2 G.E. J.79.8 Turbo-jets	22.11.61	1,606.4
G. Mossolov	E.166	P.166	7. 7.62	1,665.9
Colonel Robert L. Stephen Lt. Col. Daniel Andre (U.S.A.F.)	Lockheed YF.12A	2 Pratt & Whitney J.58 Turbojets 30,000 lb. static thrust each	1. 5.65	2,062

WORLD'S AIR SPEED RECORDS (SEAPLANES)

(The Fédération Aéronautique Internationale lists landplane and seaplane records separately. There is, therefore, some overlapping of dates but either type of aircraft holds the Absolute Air Speed Record.)

Pilot	Aircraft	Engine	Date	Speed m.p.h.
de Bernacchi (Italian)	Macchi M.52	Fiat	4.11.27	297.8
de Bernacchi (Italian)	Macchi M.52	Fiat	30. 3.28	318.6
A. H. Orlebar (British)	Supermarine S.6	Rolls-Royce (R)	12. 9.29	357.7
G. H. Stainforth (British)	Supermarine S.6B	Rolls-Royce (R)	29. 3.31	406.99
F. Agello (Italian)	Macchi 72	Fiat AS.6	23.10.34	440.67

It will be seen that from 30 March 1928 until 30 March 1939, eleven years to the day, the speed record was held entirely by seaplanes. After that date no further attempts were ever made by this type of aircraft.

BIBLIOGRAPHY

MILLIONS of words, often somewhat disconnected, have been put on paper in respect of the problems of supersonic flight. A student with all eternity ahead might profitably search out the entire range of published material but it hardly seems worth the effort. Here is a selection of published papers and articles which have proved valuable to those closely connected with the development of the SST and its ultimate operation.

REPORT OF THE S.S.T. SYMPOSIUM. International Federation of Air Line Pilots Association, London, November 1963.

TECHNICAL COMMITTEE MEETING, THE S.S.T. International Air Transport Association, Montreal, February 1961.

I.C.A.O. AND THE TECHNICAL PROBLEMS ASSOCIATED WITH THE S.S.T. International Civil Aviation Organisation, the Secretariat, Draft Document 8366-AN/880. October 10 1963.

THE X-15 PROJECT. John V. Becker in *Aeronautics and Astronautics,* March 1964.

LOCKHEED S.S.T. FEATURES DOUBLE-DELTA WING. Harold D. Watkins, in *Aviation Week and Space Technology,* March 23 1964.

VARIABLE SWEEP WING KEYNOTES BOEING 733. C. M. Plattner in *Aviation Week and Space Technology,* May 4 1964.

INFLUENCE OF AIRPLANE CONFIGURATION ON SONIC BOOM CHARACTERISTICS. Harry W. Carlson, N.A.S.A., A.I.A.A., publication, Vol. 1. No. 2.

AIR NAVIGATION PLAN, NORTH ATLANTIC REGION. I.C.A.O. Document 7674/4.

SYMPOSIUM ON ELECTRONIC RESEARCH AND DEVELOPMENT FOR CIVIL AVIATION. The Royal Radar Establishment, Ministry of Aviation, September 1963.

PROBLEMS IN THE NAVIGATION OF SUPERSONIC AIRCRAFT. Major W. L. Polhemus in the *Journal of the Institute of Navigation,* London, October 1963.

PRACTICAL CONSIDERATIONS IN COMMERCIAL S.S.T. FLIGHT OPERATIONS. Donald W. Richardson, Hughes Aircraft Corporation. A.I.A.A. Paper 64-343.

SPEED AND SAFETY IN CIVIL AVIATION. Bo Lundberg, The Aeronautical Research Institute of Sweden. Reports 94–96, August 1962.

THE EFFECT OF FUTURE DEVELOPMENTS IN AERONAUTICS ON AIR TRAFFIC CONTROL. Handel Davies and Captain V. A. M. Hunt, R.A.E. A.I.A.A. Preprint 63–466, Boston, October 1963.

BOUNDARY LAYER EFFECTS IN AERODYNAMICS. N.P.L. *Symposium,* Spring 1955 (H.M. Stationery Office, 1955.)

MACH ONE, by Michael Lithgow (Panther Books, London, 1955).

THE CROWDED SKY, by Neville Duke and Edward Lanchbery (Corgi Books, London, 1964).

INDEX